WOODWORKING FOR INDUSTRY STUDENT GUIDE

Compliments of

Keyed to the textbook

CHAS. A. BENNETT CO., Inc.

WOODWORKING FOR INDUSTRY

809 W. Detweiller Drive

Third Edition · PEORIA, ILLINOIS 61614

by John L. Feirer

After you have had an opportunity to examine this title, we would appreciate receiving your evaluation. If you would like to share this publication with others, please do so.

(PLEASE RETURN THIS TEXT IF IT DOES NOT FIT YOUR CURRICULUM)

CHAS. A. BENNETT CO., INC.

PEORIA, ILLINOIS 61614

79 80 81 82 83 D 5 4 3 2 1

ISBN 87002-300-4

CONTENTS

TO THE TEACHER

These study units are designed for use with the textbook WOODWORKING FOR INDUSTRY, Third Edition. They are planned as teaching *and* learning aids.

Notice that each study unit is divided into two parts. The first, titled "Reviewing the Main Ideas," is a series of *simple* statements designed to emphasize the important points of the text. It is an effective approach to self-instruction. It has been found in the development of material for teaching machines that completing a series of very simple statements is a highly effective way to learn.

The second part, titled "Checking Your Knowledge," is a series of more difficult objective test items to reinforce the learning and to check the student on his or her accomplishment.

Special effort has been made to integrate the best practices in language arts and mathematics with the activities that go on in the shop or laboratory. This student guide is planned so that the study units can be used by students individually or in group activity.

Students can be asked to complete these study units in one of several ways:

1. Each student may progress at his or her own rate of speed and complete the sheets as fast as possible.

2. The teacher may assign a lesson in the textbook as homework and then use the study unit for objective testing the next day.

3. Students may spend some time in supervised study covering the related information of the course.

4. Students can be assigned sections of the textbook for outside study and at the same time may be asked to complete the study units.

Other material has been included that will simplify the teaching and be of value in:

1. Organizing the class.
2. Keeping records of cost of materials.
3. Having an accurate safety record.
4. Keeping the results of student planning together.

There is also space on page 8 for additional shop regulations. All the written material for the course in woodworking can be kept in one place in a well-organized fashion.

TO THE STUDENT

How to Use This Guide

This student guide includes study units and all other material you need for keeping a record of your progress in woodworking.

Complete the following:

1. Fill in the *Student Information Sheet* (page 7). This will help your teacher become better acquainted with you.

2. Keep a record of your assignments in the student personnel and cleanup organization of your class.

3. Make a list of the shop regulations that you are expected to follow.

4. Read the safety pledge carefully. Sign it after you have agreed to obey the regulations.

5. Fill in the cost of materials chart, pages 10 and 11.

These costs will be used when making the bill of materials for each project.

6. Make a plan for each product you build.

7. Fill in each study unit. The textbook pages you should study are given at the top left-hand side of each sheet. If this guide belongs to you, place the answers in the blank spaces along the right edge of each page.

Important: If you don't own the guide, keep a record of these answers on a blank sheet in the order given in the study units. You will find there are seven different kinds of questions. Here are samples of each kind. Study each one so you will know the correct way to answer each question:

1. TRUE-FALSE. Read the statement carefully and decide if it is true or false. In the space at the right of the question, place a T for the true questions and an F for the false ones.

SAMPLE: Washington, D.C., is the capital of the United States. T or F   _____ *T* _____

2. MULTIPLE CHOICE. Read the question and the four possible answers. Select the best or correct answer and place the letter for this in the space at the right.

SAMPLE: The following state is east of the Mississippi River: (a) Arkansas, (b) Missouri, (c) Illinois, (d) Iowa.

_____ *c* _____

3. COMPLETION. Study the sentence and decide the correct word or words to finish the sentence. Write your answer in the space(s) at the right.

SAMPLE: Milk is to cow as egg is to _____.

SAMPLE: The primary colors are _____, _____, and _____.

chicken

red

yellow

blue

4. MATCHING. Match the terms in the left-hand column with those in the right-hand column. Show your choice by placing the correct numbers in the spaces at the right.

SAMPLE: Match the kinds of equipment at the left to the games at the right:

a. goal posts	1. football
b. hoop	2. tennis
c. puck	3. hockey
d. racquet	4. basketball

a. _____ *1* _____

b. _____ *4* _____

c. _____ *3* _____

d. _____ *2* _____

5. IDENTIFICATION. In the proper space at the right, place the correct name of each item shown.

SAMPLE: Identify the eating utensils shown in Sample Fig. 0-1:

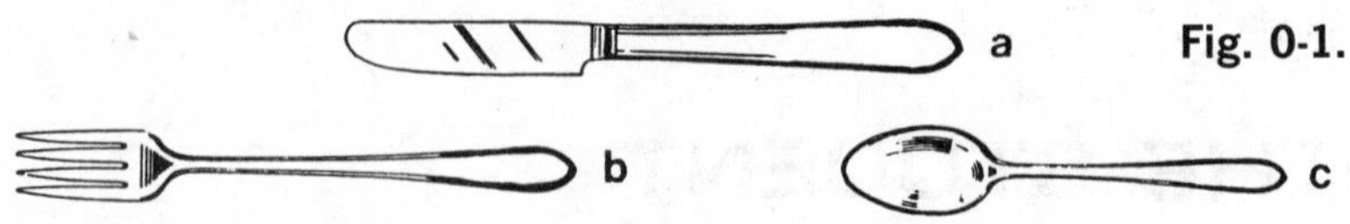

Fig. 0-1.

a. _____ *knife* _____

b. _____ *fork* _____

c. _____ *spoon* _____

6. ARRANGEMENT. Decide on the correct order of the items listed and number them accordingly in the spaces to the right.

SAMPLE: Number the following days in the order in which they occur in the week:

Thursday

Friday

Monday

_____ *2* _____

_____ *3* _____

_____ *1* _____

7. SPELLING. Some words in each list are spelled correctly; others are not. Follow the instructions which accompany each list.

SAMPLE: Check the spelling of the following words. If correct, place a "C" in the space. If incorrect, give the correct spelling.

a. Endustriul

b. Arts

c. Woodwerk

Industrial

C

Woodwork

STUDENT INFORMATION SHEET

(If this is not your book, use a separate sheet.)

Please print:

1. Name _____
                Last   First   Middle

2. Home address _____

3. Home phone number _____

4. Year _____

5. School last attended _____

6. Parents' names:

    Father _____

    Mother _____

7. Parents' occupations:

    Father employed by _____

    Mother employed by _____

8. Hobbies or outside interests _____

_____

9. Previous shop experience _____

_____

10. Name of family doctor _____

    Address _____

PERSONNEL AND CLEANUP ASSIGNMENTS

Date   **Job**

From _____ to _____   _____

From _____ to _____   _____

From _____ to _____   _____

SAFETY AND SHOP REGULATIONS

1. _____
2. _____
3. _____
4. _____
5. _____
6. _____
7. _____
8. _____
9. _____
10. _____
11. _____

SAFETY PLEDGE

I pledge that I will follow all of the safety rules given in the book WOODWORKING FOR INDUSTRY, and all of the shop regulations listed above. I will not use a power tool without first securing the permission of the instructor. I will report all accidents to the instructor immediately, no matter how small they are. I will help to maintain a safe shop by tending to my business and by not bothering other students who are busy.

Date _____   Name _____

ACCIDENT REPORT

1. Name of injured _____

   Address _____

   Telephone _____

   Home Room _____

2. Date of injury _____

3. Nature of injury (Cut, scratch, foreign matter in eye, etc.) _____

   _____

4. Tools or machines involved _____

5. Witness(es) to the accident, Name _____

   Address _____

   Name _____

   Address _____

6. Treatment: First aid _____   By whom _____

   Physician _____   Address _____

   Hospital _____   Address _____

7. Cause of accident (Poor condition of equipment, wrong procedure, etc.) _____

   _____

   _____

8. Correction (What will be done to prevent future accidents) _____

   _____

   _____

   _____
        NAME

COST OF MATERIALS

Lumber:

Kind	Cost Per Board Foot	Kind	Cost Per Board Foot
Pine			
Poplar			
Basswood			
Mahogany			
Walnut			
Maple			
Oak			
Birch			

Panel Stock:

Kind	Thickness	Cost Per Sq. Foot
Fir Plywood	1/4'' (6 mm)	
Fir Plywood	3/8'' (9.5 mm)	
Fir Plywood	1/2'' (13 mm)	
Hardboard		
Particle Board		

COST OF MATERIALS (contd.)

Screws, Nails and Other Items:

No. or Size	Kind	Cost Per _____
	Screws	
_____	_____	_____
_____		_____
	Nails	
_____	_____	_____
_____		_____
	Dowel	
_____	_____	_____
	Sandpaper	
_____	_____	_____
_____	_____	_____
	Hardware	
_____	_____	_____
_____	_____	_____
_____	_____	_____

Finishing Materials:

Kind	Cost Per _____
Stain	
Filler	
Shellac	
Penetrating Finish	
Varnish	
Enamel	

PLAN SHEET

Name_____ Grade_____

Name of the Product   Date Started   Date Completed

Bill of Materials:

Size				Name of Part	Material	Unit Cost	Total Cost
No.	T	W	L				

Tools and Machines:

_____

_____

_____

_____

_____

_____

_____

_____

_____

_____

_____

_____

_____

_____

Procedure or Steps:

1. _____

2. _____

3. _____

4. _____

5. _____

6. _____

7. _____

8. _____

9. _____

10. _____

11. _____

12. _____

13. _____

14. _____

15. _____

RECORD IN THE WOODSHOP

Class Tests

No. 1 _____   No. 4 _____

No. 2 _____   No. 5 _____

No. 3 _____   No. 6 _____

Product Grades

1 _____   5 _____
   Name   Grade   Name   Grade

2 _____   6 _____
   Name   Grade   Name   Grade

3 _____   7 _____
   Name   Grade   Name   Grade

4 _____   8 _____
   Name   Grade   Name   Grade

Study Guide No. 1
INTRODUCTION

Reviewing the Main Ideas

1. A growth material that is still one of America's most valuable and important building materials is _____.

2. Primary uses for _____ are for homes, furniture, boats, musical instruments, and sports equipment.

3. Some manufactured wood materials are plywood, _____, and particle board.

4. The technique of gluing pieces of lumber together is called _____.

5. Because we can continue to grow trees, there is a _____ abundance of supply.

6. Wood is a very durable material as is evidenced by _____ still standing that were built of wood over 200 years ago.

7. Pound for pound, wood is stronger than _____.

8. The cellular structure allows wood to insulate against cold and heat 6 times more effectively than _____.

9. Wood is a natural acoustical material, reflecting and _____ sound.

Checking Your Knowledge

1. One of the following is *not* an important manufactured wood material: (a) plywood, (b) hardboard, (c) cokeboard, (d) particle board.

2. For each individual in the United States, about _____ times more lumber is consumed than the average of world consumption.

3. One of the following is *not* an important material made from wood: (a) cloth, (b) flavoring extract, (c) chemicals, (d) leather.

4. Well built homes will last more than 200 years. T or F

5. Wood is a good conductor of electricity. T or F

6. As an insulating material, wood is better than aluminum by: (a) 2000 times, (b) 1700 times, (c) 3000 times, (d) 4000 times.

7. Wood is an easily worked material. T or F

8. Check the spelling of the following words. If correct, place a "C" in the space. If incorrect, give the correct spelling.

   a. Laminating

   b. Production

   c. Durable

   d. Noncondictor

Name_____

Score_____

Study Guide No. 2
CAREER OPPORTUNITIES

Reviewing the Main Ideas

1. Wood is one of our most important natural _____.

2. People who have extensive education and training for a specific occupation relating to wood products are called _____ craftsmen.

3. The person who works with engineers, scientists, supervisors, and skilled craftsmen in converting theories and ideas into products and processes is called a _____.

4. An example of a _____ occupation in the woodworking industry is that of a forester.

5. The largest single group of craft people in the building trades is the _____.

6. People who make preliminary plans and working drawings and supervise the projects as they are built are called _____.

7. People who teach woodwork or general shop classes, as well as carpentry, patternmaking, cabinetmaking, and boatbuilding are called _____ _____ teachers.

Checking Your Knowledge

1. One of the following is *not* a member of the construction industry team: (a) architect, (b) contractor, (c) furniture designer, (d) carpenter.

2. The education and training of a registered architect requires a minimum of seven years. T or F

3. Industrial education teachers form one of the largest groups of professional workers for which a knowledge of woodworking is important. T or F.

4. Those who make up the largest skilled trade group are the: (a) patternmakers, (b) cabinetmakers, (c) painters and finishers, (d) carpenters.

5. The following natural raw material can be renewed: (a) coal, (b) wood, (c) iron ore, (d) petroleum.

6. Carpenters comprise the largest single group of people who work in the building trades. T or F

7. One method of learning to be a carpenter is by completing a four-year apprenticeship. T or F

8. Carpenters who do exterior and interior trim work are called: (a) rough carpenters, (b) finish carpenters, (c) skilled carpenters, (d) millrights.

9. A patternmaker must understand the following area of the metal industry: (a) sheet metal, (b) machine shop, (c) foundry, (d) welding.

10. There are approximately the following number of foresters in the United States: (a) 10 000, (b) 22 000, (c) 30 000, (d) 40 000.

_____

11. A technician must usually spend at least two years in a technical institute or community junior college. T or F

_____

12. The following professional person spends a good deal of time out of doors: (a) industrial education teacher, (b) interior designer, (c) forester, (d) research worker.

_____

13. Check the spelling of the following words. If correct, place a "C" in the space. If incorrect, give the correct spelling.

a. Occupational

_____

b. Manufacturing

_____

c. Mechanecal

_____

d. Technician

_____

e. Patternmaker

_____

f. Foresters

_____

Name_____

Score_____

Study Guide No. 3
SAFETY

Reviewing the Main Ideas

1. The furniture and building industry spends millions of dollars in developing _____ programs.
_____

2. Goggles, guards, and other safety devices are a help in protecting a person from _____.
_____

3. Dress correctly for the job. Make sure there are no rings or a loose necktie that may cause _____.
_____

4. Keep the machine and the area around it _____.
_____

5. Hand tools for cutting must be kept _____ and used in the correct way for good results.
_____

6. Portable _____ tools must be grounded and used in a dry area.
_____

7. Follow the special _____ rules in operating each machine tool.
_____

8. Wear special _____ devices when grinding, spraying, or doing heavy lifting.
_____

9. Lift with your _____, not with your back.
_____

10. Use a ladder correctly and make sure you have secure _____.
_____

11. Avoid practical _____ and horseplay.
_____

12. Take care of small injuries and get proper _____ attention.
_____

13. The abbreviation for the Occupational Safety and Health Act is _____.
_____

Checking Your Knowledge

1. One of the following is an *incorrect* method of dressing for woodwork: (a) wear a short-sleeved shirt, (b) tuck in your tie, (c) roll up your sleeves, (d) wear rings and other jewelry.
_____

2. A defective portable electric drill used in a damp place can kill the operator. T or F
_____

3. All cutting operations on the circular saw can be done with a basket-type guard in place. T or F
_____

4. To lift a heavy object you should use your back muscles, not your leg muscles. T or F
_____

5. A ladder should be secured at an angle of: (a) about 90°, (b) about 75°, (c) about 50°, (d) about 60°.
_____

6. The ABC of safety is A_____ B_____ C_____.

7. Oily rags should be kept in a covered wooden container. T or F

8. Fig. 3-4 in the text shows the correct method of using a knife. T or F

9. The operator shown in Fig. 3-3 in the text is following good housekeeping practices. T or F

10. A circular saw is a better power tool for ripping than is a radial saw. T or F

11. On many construction sites, _____ hats must be worn in certain restricted areas.

12. Check the spelling of the following words. If correct, place a "C" in the space. If incorrect, give the correct spelling.

    a. Safety

    b. Hazzards

    c. Porteable

    d. Flammable

    e. Protecteve

    f. Accident

    g. Permaneant

Name_____

Score_____

Study Guide No. 4
DESIGN

Reviewing the Main Ideas

1. A product that demonstrates the *three keys* to good design will function well, have an attractive appearance, and be _____ sound.

2. _____ is all-important in wood products.

3. The elements of design are line, shape, _____, color, and tones and texture.

4. Straight, curved, and S-shaped are common kinds of _____.

5. Square, round, rectangular, and triangular are common _____.

6. The principles of design include proportion, _____, harmony, rhythm, and emphasis.

7. A ratio of 5:8 is considered nearly perfect _____.

8. The way various parts of an object blend together describes _____.

9. The three most popular styles of American furniture are modern or contemporary, _____, and early American or colonial.

10. Home design includes the landscape, individual room design, and the design of the _____ itself.

11. Structural design involves how well the product is _____ and whether it serves its purpose.

12. The history of furniture designs closely parallels the history of _____.

13. The bed is the oldest piece of furniture. It was developed by the _____.

14. The best furniture designs in China were developed during the _____ period.

15. Mahogany was first imported into England in the year _____.

_____

_____

_____

_____

_____

_____

_____

_____

_____

_____

_____

_____

_____

_____

_____

Checking Your Knowledge

1. Match the design principles at the left to the word descriptions at the right:

   a. balance
   b. harmony
   c. rhythm
   d. proportion
   e. emphasis

   1. formal and informal
   2. 5:8 relationship
   3. blends together
   4. point of interest
   5. repetition

   a. _____

   b. _____

   c. _____

   d. _____

   e. _____

2. How good is your design judgment? Study the following illustration (Fig. 4-1) and tell which of each pair, L or R, is better designed.

a. _____

b. _____

c. _____

d. _____

e. _____

f. _____

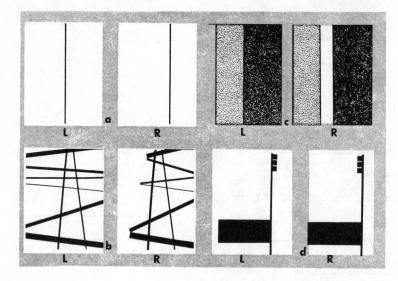

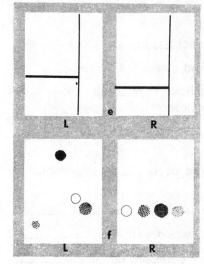

Fig. 4-1.

3. Name the four common kinds of lines shown in Fig. 4-2:

a. _____

b. _____

c. _____

d. _____

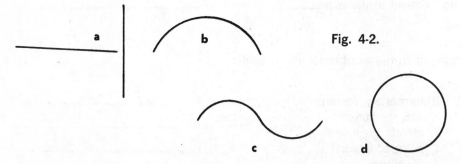

Fig. 4-2.

4. If the short dimension of a mirror frame must be 14 inches, then the length should be _____ inches to give the frame good proportion.

_____

5. If a vertical line through the center of an object will divide it symmetrically or equally on both sides, then it is said to have _____ balance.

_____

6. Identify the three popular furniture styles shown in the text in Fig. 4-12 (a, b, and c):

    a. _____

    b. _____

    c. _____

7. Name the four common shapes shown in Fig. 4-3:

    a. _____

    b. _____

    c. _____

    d. _____

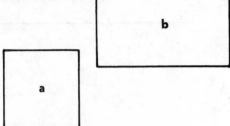 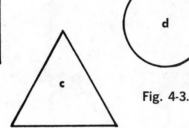

Fig. 4-3.

8. Fig. 4-4 indicates six colors described as primary in text Fig. 4-6. Name them.

    a. _____

    b. _____

    c. _____

    d. _____

    e. _____

    f. _____

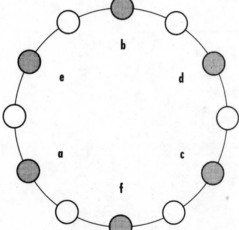

9. When yellow and blue are mixed together they produce _____.

10. When yellow and red are mixed together they produce _____.

Fig. 4-4.

11. When a colored surface reflects light it produces a _____.

_____

12. When speaking of color, the pattern of contrasts in light reflections is known as texture. T or F

_____

13. The combination of the best of the 18th-century designers is known as _____ design.

_____

14. One of the following is *not* a common regional style of home in the United States: (a) Cape Cod, (b) Western Modern, (c) French Provincial, (d) Colonial.

_____

15. One of the following is *not* among developments in structural design in house construction: (a) trussed roofs, (b) box beams, (c) timbers, (d) stressed skin panels.

_____

16. Check the spelling of the following words. If correct, place a "C" in the space. If incorrect, give the correct spelling.

a. Design _____

b. Triengular _____

c. Dimensionel _____

d. Harmonious _____

e. Proprotion _____

f. Symmetrically _____

g. Harmony _____

Name_____

Score_____

Study Guide No. 5
METRICS IN WOODWORK

Reviewing the Main Ideas

1. Two widely used systems of measurement are the customary and the _____ system.

2. The number of base units in the SI metric system is _____.

3. A metre is the base unit of _____ in the metric system.

4. There are 1000 millimetres in a _____.

5. The cubic decimetre, when used as a unit of liquid capacity, is called the _____.

6. A litre is approximately six percent more than a _____.

7. A kilogram equals 1000 _____.

8. One inch is exactly 25.4 _____.

9. Water boils at 100 degrees Celsius on the _____ scale.

10. The metric system is a _____ system like our money.

Checking Your Knowledge

1. The customary (English) system of measurement is used throughout most of the world. T or F

2. The symbol for the modernized metric system is: (a) ISO, (b) IS, (c) SI, (d) MM.

3. One of the following is *not* among commonly used everyday units in the metric system: (a) length—metre, (b) weight—kilogram, (c) pressure—pascal, (d) liquid volume—litre.

4. The correct symbol for millimetre is: (a) MM, (b) mm, (c) mm., (d) Mn.

5. One inch (1″) equals exactly this many millimetres: (a) 25.4, (b) 25, (c) 22, (d) 24.5.

6. The best type of metric rule to use is one with the numbered lines marked in: (a) dekametres, (b) millimetres, (c) centimetres, (d) decimetres.

7. A litre is larger than a quart. T or F

8. Six millimetres is about the same as: (a) 1/4″, (b) 1/8″, (c) 1/16″, (d) 1/32″.

9. One millimetre is between the following customary measurements in size: (a) 1/4″ to 1/2″, (b) 1/8″ to 1/4″, (c) 1/16″ to 1/8″, (d) 1/32″ to 1/16″.

10. A 300-millimetre rule is longer than a 1-foot rule. T or F

11. Match the seven base units at the left to the correct symbols at the right:

a. metre   1. A
b. kilogram   2. s
c. second   3. K
d. ampere   4. kg
e. kelvin   5. m
f. candela   6. mol
g. mole   7. cd

a. _____
b. _____
c. _____
d. _____
e. _____
f. _____
g. _____

12. The following expression is both metric and decimal: (a) 1/4 metre, (b) 9.5 inches, (c) 6.3 mm, (d) 3 pounds.

_____

13. A kilogram is approximately: (a) 1 pound, (b) 1.5 pounds, (c) 2.2 pounds, (d) 3 pounds.

_____

14. About half the world's population now uses the metric system. T or F

_____

15. The metric system is a decimal system based on units of: (a) five, (b) ten, (c) fifteen, (d) twenty.

_____

16. The metre rule is longer than a yardstick by: (a) 2″, (b) 3.37″, (c) 4″, (d) 5″.

_____

17. Skilled workers in one of the following industries must be among the first to know and use the metric system: (a) furniture construction, (b) patternmaking, (c) home building, (d) painting and finishing.

_____

18. There is a great need for metric standards in the furniture industry. T or F

_____

19. The recommended standard building module in the metric system is: (a) 150 mm, (b) 250 mm, (c) 100 mm, (d) 450 mm.

_____

20. Check the spelling of the following words. If correct, place a "C" in the space. If incorrect, give the correct spelling.

a. Convarsion

_____

b. Metric

_____

c. Modueles

_____

d. Kilogrem

_____

e. Degrees Celsius

_____

Study Guide No. 6
READING PRINTS, ESTIMATING, AND PLANNING

Reviewing the Main Ideas

1. In all woodworking, the ability to read and understand _____, prints, and plans is basic.

2. Ideas of designers and architects are expressed in drawings by means of lines, symbols, and _____.

3. A good woodworker must be able to read and interpret the sketch, _____, or print correctly.

4. An exact copy of the drawing is called a _____.

5. The building industry makes use of prints called _____.

6. In multiview or _____ projection drawings, views are not always in their proper position.

7. The four types of drawings used in cabinet-making are _____, cabinet, perspective, and isometric.

8. Views of a _____ are shown as general and detail drawings.

9. The plans and elevations are _____ drawings.

10. Sectionals and sections are _____ drawings.

11. The plan showing the outline of the lot and the location of the building is called the _____ or plot plan.

12. The top view of the footings or foundation walls is called a foundation or _____ plan.

13. The cross-section view of a house showing (among other things) the outside shape of the building is called a building or _____ plan.

14. The plans that show the size, number, location, and spacing of the structural members are called _____ plans.

15. External views of the house made from the front, rear, right, and left sides are called _____.

16. Views that show how a house would look if it were cut vertically are called _____ views or sections.

17. Important information that cannot be given by dimensions, such as kinds of materials, is given by using _____.

18. Drawings for patternmaking follow the standard rules used in the _____ trades.

19. Every woodworker must know how to determine the amount of materials needed, and this is called _____.

_____

_____

_____

_____

_____

_____

_____

_____

_____

_____

_____

_____

_____

_____

_____

_____

_____

_____

_____

20. Lumber is sold by the _____ foot.

21. Plywood, hardboard, particle board, sheathing, wallboard, and similar materials are sold by the _____ foot.

22. To build a piece of furniture, you need a drawing or _____, list of materials, and plan of procedure.

23. In the building construction industry, the needed items for building a house include a set of prints, a detailed material list or bill of _____, and a set of complete specifications.

24. In the metric system, all dimensions are shown in millimetres except for _____ plans.

25. When both inches and millimetres are shown on the drawing itself, it is called _____ dimensioning.

Checking Your Knowledge

1. In the building industry most prints are: (a) dry diazo, (b) ozalid, (c) blueprint, (d) moist diazo.

2. An advantage of blueprints is that they can be exposed to _____ without fading.

3. A woodworking drawing is frequently a combination of several types of drawings. T or F

4. Another name for a multiview drawing is _____.

5. Identify the symbols for the kinds of materials shown in Fig. 6-1:

a. _____

b. _____

c. _____

d. _____

e. _____

f. _____

g. _____

h. _____

i. _____

j. _____

k. _____

l. _____

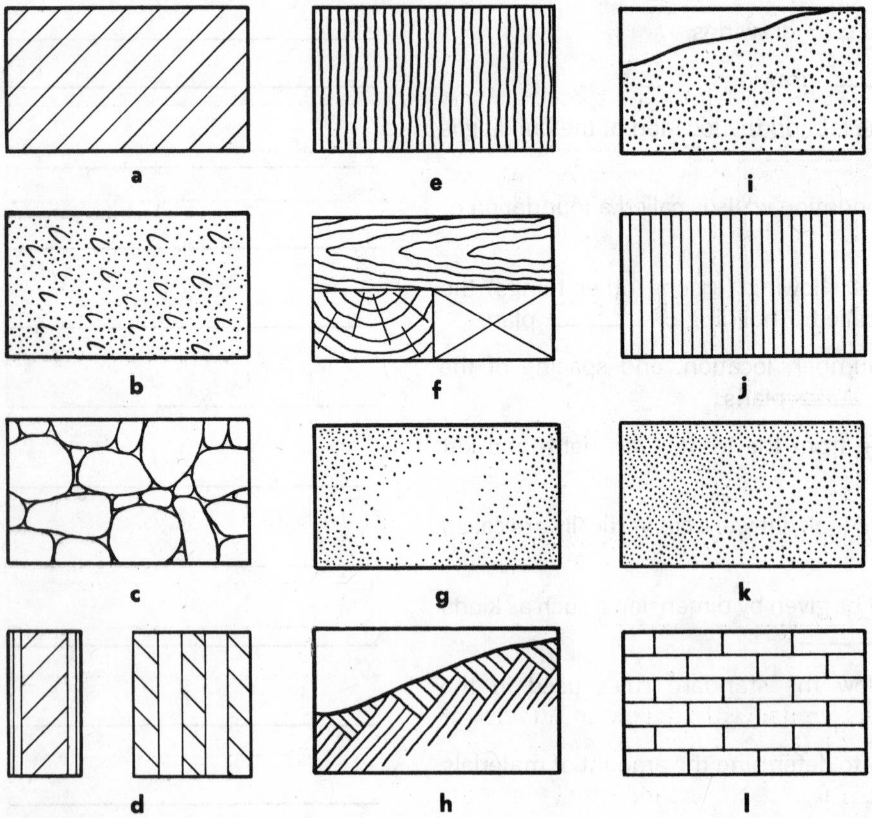

Fig. 6-1.

28

6. The floor plan of a house is a: (a) detail drawing, (b) general drawing, (c) isometric drawing, (d) cabinet drawing.   _____

7. A scale commonly used for general drawings is 1/16″ = 1′ 0″. T or F   _____

8. A house plan that is drawn 1 1/2 inches to 1 foot is 1/8 full size. T or F   _____

9. A perspective drawing of a house showing how it looks when it is completed is called a presentation drawing or a pictorial _____.   _____

10. To find the size and shape of the rooms of a house you would check: (a) site plan, (b) building plan, (c) top plan, (d) foundation plan.   _____

11. One of the following is *not* a common type of drawing used in cabinet-making: (a) multiview drawing, (b) cabinet drawing, (c) cavalier drawing, (d) isometric drawing.   _____

12. Identify symbols for doors and windows shown in Fig. 6-2:

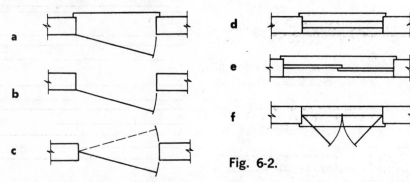

Fig. 6-2.

a. _____
b. _____
c. _____
d. _____
e. _____
f. _____

13. Name the symbols for plumbing fixtures shown in Fig. 6-3:

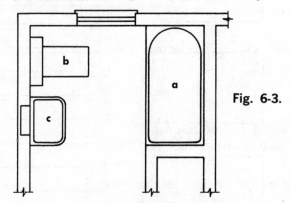

Fig. 6-3.

a. _____
b. _____
c. _____

14. How many feet of 8-inch material would be needed to cover an opening of 10 square feet?   _____

15. The common size of plywood sheet is _____ x _____.   _____

_____

16. The common size hardboard sheet contains the following number of square feet: (a) 20, (b) 24, (c) 32, (d) 36.   _____

17. A square of shingles will normally cover _____ square feet of roof area.   _____

18. Identify the symbols for electrical wiring shown in Fig. 6-4:

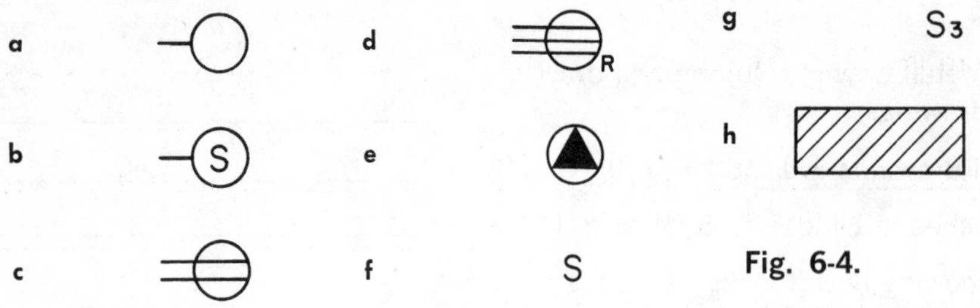

a   ─○

b   ─Ⓢ

c   ═◯

d   ═◯ᵣ

e   ▲

f   S

g S_3

h   ▨

Fig. 6-4.

a. _____

b. _____

c. _____

d. _____

e. _____

f. _____

g. _____

h. _____

19. Tell how many feet of 10-inch material are needed to cover an opening that measures 4 x 5 feet.

_____

20. Study Figs. 6-18a, 6-18b, and 6-19 in the text and complete these statements:

a. The drawer fronts are made of _____ _____ plywood.

b. The drawer bottoms are made of _____ plywood.

c. This desk contains _____ (number) drawers.

d. Including the facing, the overall size of the top is _____ inches by _____ inches.

e. The overall height of the desk is _____ inches.

f. The finished size of the legs is _____ inches (thickness) by _____ inches (width) by _____ inches (length).

_____

_____

_____

_____

_____

_____

_____

g. The ends of the legs are cut off at an angle of _____ degrees.

h. The legs taper a total of _____ inches in width.

i. The height of drawer number 4 is _____ inches.

_____

_____

_____

21. Study the set of architectural drawings appearing on textbook pages 82–97, the material list (page 103), and specifications (page 108), and complete the following:

a. Give the size (thickness and width of material) to be used for the following wood members:

(1) girders _____ x _____

(2) ceiling joists _____ x _____

(3) rafters _____ x _____

_____

_____

_____

_____

b. The overall size of the living room is _____ x _____.   _____

                                                                        _____

c. The overall size of the house is _____ x _____.   _____

                                                                        _____

d. The footings for the house must be a mixture of one part Portland   _____
    cement; three parts of clean, coarse, sharp sand free from _____
    or vegetable matter, and 5 parts of 3/4-inch gravel.   _____

e. The sink should measure _____ by _____.   _____

                                                                        _____

f. The linen closet has _____ (number) shelves.   _____

g. The front door should measure _____ by _____.   _____

                                                                        _____

h. The opening in the front of the fireplace should measure _____ by _____
    _____.
                                                                        _____

                                                                        _____

i. The ceiling joists are placed _____ inches on center.   _____

j. The wardrobe in the large bedroom has _____ type doors.   _____

k. There are _____ (number) convenience outlets in the living room.   _____

l. There are _____ (number) window openings in the basement.   _____

m. The width of the stairway to the basement is _____ inches.   _____

n. The door on the clothes closet near the entrance should measure
    _____ by _____.   _____

                                                                        _____

o. There are two types of windows in the living room, the _____ and
    the _____ _____.   _____

                                                                        _____

p. _____ (number) windows in the living room can be opened for
    ventilation.   _____

q. The exterior material used on the front of the house is V-joint _____
    _____.   _____

r. The materials used on the side of the house behind the fireplace
    chimney are _____ _____ _____.   _____

s. All floor joists are to be _____ inches on center.   _____

t. The footing sizes are to conform to local soil conditions and _____
    _____.   _____

u. The bridging used on the floor joists should be _____ by _____ inches.

_____

_____

v. The scale of the detail drawing shown for sections A and B is _____ equals _____.

_____

22. A 14-inch dimension is about 460 millimetres. T or F

_____

23. Check the spelling of the following words. If correct, place a "C" in the space. If incorrect, give the correct spelling.

a. Multiview

_____

b. Orthegraphic

_____

c. Perspective

_____

d. Isometric

_____

e. Specifications

_____

Study Guide No. 7
WOOD PROCESSING

Reviewing the Main Ideas

1. Another name for the raw material from _____ is lumber. _____

2. Material from trees that require additional processing is called _____ stock. _____

3. The arm of a chair is a good example of a standard part, or _____. _____

4. A roof truss for building a house is a good example of a _____. _____

5. A coffee table in its final form is an example of a _____ product. _____

6. Sawdust is one of the _____ from wood. _____

7. Material processing falls into _____ basic classifications. _____

8. Cutting of wood is sometimes called _____. _____

9. Kiln drying of wood is a process called _____. _____

10. The thin groove caused by sawing is called a _____. _____

11. A cutting process in which no chips are formed is called _____. _____

12. Using sandpaper to wear away a surface is a process known as _____. _____

13. A forming method that uses thin veneers is called _____. _____

14. Bending without heat is done by a process called _____. _____

15. Fastening is sometimes called assembling or _____. _____

16. Gluing with adhesives is also known as _____. _____

17. The process of applying some kind of finishing material is called _____. _____

Checking Your Knowledge

1. One of the following is *not* a material included in standard stock: (a) wood paneling, (b) window frames, (c) hardboard, (d) particle board. _____

2. Plywood is considered to be standard stock. T or F _____

3. The leg of a table is considered to be standard stock. T or F _____

4. Standard parts are made from _____ _____. _____

5. Another name for standard parts is _____. _____

6. One of the following is *not* a standard part: (a) table leg, (b) chair arm, (c) the turned rung of a chair, (d) the three-legged base of a plant stand. _____

7. Subassemblies are combined to make up the finished product. T or F _____

8. One of the following is *not* a common subassembly: (a) a table top, (b) a chair back with rails, (c) a door set in a frame, (d) a window unit. _____

9. Match the words at the left to the items they describe at the right:

   a. finished product   1. chair leg
   b. component   2. chair
   c. subassembly   3. hardboard
   d. standard stock   4. roof truss

   a. _____

   b. _____

   c. _____

   d. _____

10. Processing of wood produces many _____.

    _____

11. Oils, sawdust, and wood chips are some of the _____ of wood processing.

    _____

12. Materials resulting from wood processing are waste products. T or F

    _____

13. In converting trees into wood products, the number of processes involved is: (a) five, (b) three, (c) four, (d) six.

    _____

14. Before wood can be processed, it must be _____ dried or _____ dried.

    _____

15. One of the following is *not* a way in which wood is sawed: (a) reciprocal, (b) rotary, (c) continuous, (d) routing.

    _____

16. Veneers are cut from a log by the _____ process.

    _____

17. Wood is always planed by machine. T or F

    _____

18. Abrading is *not* done in one of the following ways: (a) on a jointer, (b) on a belt sander, (c) by hand with sandpaper, (d) on a disc sander.

    _____

19. Match the types of wood processing at the left to the descriptions at the right:

    a. routing and shaping   1. done on a wood lathe
    b. drilling and boring   2. used to form the edge or surface
    c. wood grinding   with rotary cutters
    d. turning   3. cutting holes in wood
        4. reducing wood to flour or chips

    a. _____

    b. _____

    c. _____

    d. _____

20. Routing and shaping are always done by machine. T or F

    _____

21. Hardboard and particle board are products which have developed as a result of the process of: (a) abrading, (b) turning, (c) shearing, (d) grinding.

    _____

22. Plywood is an example of lamination. T or F

    _____

23. As wood is conditioned by steam, it becomes easier to bend. T or F

    _____

24. In the kerfing process, wood is bent without heat. T or F

    _____

25. Match the processes at the left to the descriptions at the right:

    a. extruding   1. wood flour combined with adhesive
    b. flour molding
    c. mat forming   2. used to produce hardboard and particle board
        3. material forced through a die to produce wood panels

    a. _____

    b. _____

    c. _____

26. Match the common methods of fastening and assembling at the left to the descriptions at the right:

    a. mechanical fastening
    b. joinery
    c. bonding

    1. use of nails, screws, and other fasteners
    2. use of adhesives
    3. use of joints

    a. _____
    b. _____
    c. _____

27. There are _____ common methods of assembling or combining.

    _____

28. One of the following is *not* a mechanical fastener: (a) dovetail joint, (b) screws, (c) nails, (d) dowels.

    _____

29. In the bonding method of assembly, both heat and pressure are required. T or F

    _____

30. Match the wood finishing procedures at the left to the descriptions at the right:

    a. coating
    b. refinishing
    c. texturing
    d. coloring
    e. covering

    1. applying stains
    2. charring, grooving, and sand-blasting
    3. applying lacquer, shellac, or varnish
    4. removing an old finish
    5. adding material to wood surfaces to improve wearing quality

    a. _____
    b. _____
    c. _____
    d. _____
    e. _____

31. A finishing material which enters the wood pores is called a _____ finish.

    _____

32. One of the following is *not* a surface finisher: (a) varnish, (b) shellac, (c) lacquer, (d) fiberglass.

    _____

33. Check the spelling of the following words. If correct, place a "C" in the space. If incorrect, give the correct spelling.

    a. Compenontes

    _____

    b. Separeting

    _____

    c. Recipocal

    _____

    d. Abrading

    _____

    e. Conditioning

    _____

    f. Pleable

    _____

Name_____

Score_____

Study Guide No. 8
KINDS OF WOODS

Reviewing the Main Ideas

1. A wood plant that grows at least 20 feet (6.7 m) tall is called a _____.   _____

2. Climbing woody vines are called _____.   _____

3. There are about _____ commercially important woods in North America.   _____

4. It is important to be able to _____ different kinds of woods.   _____

5. The official wood identification agency of the United States Government is the _____ _____ _____ at Madison, Wisconsin.   _____

6. The hardwoods are classified as the _____ species.   _____

7. Some of the most widely used _____ include black cherry, oak, yellow birch, Philippine mahogany, authentic mahogany, and walnut.   _____

8. Softwoods are the _____ species.   _____

9. Some of the most common varieties of _____ are redwood, ponderosa pine, sugar pine, western white pine, and Douglas fir.   _____

Checking Your Knowledge

1. Match the woods at the left to the uses at the right:

a. American beech	1. shingles
b. rock elm	2. food containers
c. white ash	3. dance floors
d. white oak	4. wood patterns
e. yellow birch	5. piano sounding boards
f. sugar maple	6. softwood plywood
g. authentic mahogany	7. barrels, kegs, and casks
h. western red cedar	8. bent parts of chairs
i. Sitka spruce	9. long oars
j. Douglas fir	10. spools and bobbins

a. _____

b. _____

c. _____

d. _____

e. _____

f. _____

g. _____

h. _____

i. _____

j. _____

2. Red cedar is a common hardwood. T or F   _____

3. One of the following is *not* a common softwood: (a) redwood, (b) Sitka spruce, (c) sweet gum, (d) western red cedar.   _____

4. Redwood is often used in making hardwood floors. T or F   _____

5. One type of authentic mahogany is native to the Philippine Islands. T or F

      _____

6. A major source of authentic mahogany is Africa. T or F

      _____

7. Most western white pine lumber is used in building construction. T or F

      _____

8. A principal use of western red cedar is for shingles. T or F

      _____

9. One of the following is *not* a kind of authentic mahogany: (a) African, (b) Tropical American, (c) Malayan, (d) Cuban.

      _____

10. American basswood is classified as a broad-leaf species. T or F

      _____

11. The botanical name of black walnut is: (a) Prunus serotina, (b) Carya, (c) Quercus, (d) Juglans nigra.

      _____

12. A wood sample from any unusual source can be sent for identification to the _____ _____ _____.

      _____

13. A wood especially suited to flooring for bowling alleys and dance floors is _____ _____.

      _____

14. Most softwood plywoods are made from: (a) western larch, (b) white fir, (c) western hemlock, (d) Douglas fir.

      _____

15. Check the spelling of the following words. If correct, place a "C" in the space. If incorrect, give the correct spelling.

    a. Labarotary

      _____

    b. Sycamore

      _____

    c. Hickery

      _____

    d. Phillipine

      _____

    e. Ponderosa

      _____

    f. Douglas

      _____

    g. Engleman

      _____

Study Guide No. 9
PROPERTIES OF WOODS

Reviewing the Main Ideas

1. It is important to know the _____ of wood before you can select the correct one for a particular use.

2. Attractive appearance and desirable wood grain are essential in _____ construction.

3. Two very desirable furniture _____ are mahogany and walnut.

4. The ability of a wood to resist denting, scratching, and cutting is called _____.

5. The weight of wood is a good indicator of the relative _____ of wood.

6. Wood _____ as it dries.

7. Wood _____ as it gets damp.

8. Bow, crook, cup, and twist are kinds of _____.

9. Woods such as oak and maple are difficult to work with _____ tools.

10. A denser and harder wood usually holds _____ better.

11. The ability of a piece of lumber to carry a load when it is placed in a horizontal position with the ends resting on two or more supports is called _____ _____.

12. Resistance to bending under a load is called _____.

13. The ability to resist being squeezed together is called the _____ _____.

14. When wood can withstand a sudden shock load, it means that it has good _____.

15. Wood that is kept fairly dry will resist _____ and last almost indefinitely.

16. In general, wood that is plain sawed has a better _____ _____ than that which is quartersawed.

Checking Your Knowledge

1. Yellow pine is a good wood to use in making bats for professional baseball. T or F

2. One of the following is *not* among things to be considered in selecting fine furniture woods: (a) good appearance, (b) attractive color, (c) low cost, (d) minimum warpage.

3. Teakwood is a very hard and abrasive material. T or F

4. Maple has a hardness of surface that is uniform throughout. T or F

     _____

5. Softwoods, as classified by species, are often harder than some hardwoods. T or F

     _____

6. An extremely light wood often used for model building is _____.

     _____

7. Wood shrinks and swells relatively more in length than it does in width. T or F

     _____

8. Twist is one type of warp. T or F

     _____

9. An increase of one inch in the height of a 10-inch beam will increase its bending strength by _____ percent.

     _____

10. Hardwoods with high bending strength are not used in home construction because of their high cost. T or F

     _____

11. A 10-inch joist standing on edge is twice as stiff as an 8-inch joist. T or F

     _____

12. The stiffness of wood is affected by such defects as knots, checks, and shake. T or F

     _____

13. Compression strength is very important in selecting wood for use in plank-and-beam construction. T or F

     _____

14. One of the following woods does *not* have a high toughness, or resistance to shock: (a) hickory, (b) birch, (c) oak, (d) basswood.

     _____

15. The best of all woods for toughness is _____.

     _____

16. *Dry rot* is a good description of decay. T or F

     _____

17. One method of preventing wood from decaying is to treat it with preservatives. T or F

     _____

18. The surface appearance, or figure, of red gum is due to its: (a) wavy or curly grain, (b) coloring matter, (c) flakes or rays, (d) method of cutting.

     _____

19. Wood must be painted or it will soon decay. T or F

     _____

20. Most paint failures in homes are due to improper venting to remove interior moisture. T or F

     _____

21. The relative hardness of one of the following hardwoods is low: (a) black walnut, (b) black cherry, (c) white oak, (d) cottonwood.

     _____

22. The relative hardness of one of the following softwoods is high: (a) sugar pine, (b) white fir, (c) western white pine, (d) western larch.

     _____

23. One of the following hardwoods is *not* comparatively heavy: (a) yellow birch, (b) sugar maple, (c) American beech, (d) basswood.

     _____

24. The comparative weight of sugar pine is low. T or F

     _____

25. One of the following hardwoods is rated relatively good in its freedom from shrinking and swelling: (a) mahogany, (b) rock elm, (c) basswood, (d) sweet gum.

     _____

26. A major value of redwood as a building construction material is that it is relatively free from shrinking and swelling. T or F

     _____

27. One of the following hardwoods is *not* free from warping: (a) black walnut, (b) black cherry, (c) yellow poplar, (d) rock elm.

     _____

28. As a group, softwoods are freer of warpage than hardwoods. T or F   _____

29. A good wood for making a product with hand tools is: (a) Philippine mahogany, (b) red oak, (c) yellow birch, (d) American elm.   _____

30. Sugar pine is an easy wood to work with hand tools. T or F   _____

31. One of the following woods has a low nail-holding power: (a) yellow birch, (b) cottonwood, (c) American elm, (d) white ash.   _____

32. White fir has low nail-holding power. T or F   _____

33. A good wood for a joist (on the basis of the comparative bending strength) would *not* be: (a) Douglas fir, (b) western larch, (c) Engelmann spruce, (d) shortleaf pine.   _____

34. Rock elm is high in stiffness. T or F   _____

35. One reason for the popularity of redwood in plank-and-beam construction is that it has high compression strength. T or F   _____

36. Many modern homes have an exterior of mahogany or redwood because these woods have high resistance to decay. T or F   _____

37. The amount of figure in basswood is high. T or F   _____

38. Yellow birch is a relatively easy wood on which to apply a finish. T or F   _____

39. The following is the lightest wood in weight: (a) cottonwood, (b) balsa, (c) American sycamore, (d) Sitka spruce.   _____

40. An extremely heavy wood is: (a) American elm, (b) sweet gum, (c) quebracho, (d) ponderosa pine.   _____

41. A wood that has little figure and is difficult to finish is: (a) American beech, (b) basswood, (c) white oak, (d) yellow birch.   _____

42. A hardwood that can be easily worked with hand tools is: (a) rock elm, (b) white ash, (c) sugar maple, (d) yellow poplar.   _____

43. Fig. 9-1 is a good illustration of _____ _____.   _____

Fig. 9-1.

44. The wood used for a baseball bat must have high: (a) surface figure, (b) compression strength, (c) toughness, (d) stiffness.

_____

45. A springboard must rate high in: (a) weight, (b) hardness, (c) stiffness, (d) compression strength.

_____

46. A softwood that has a large amount of figure is: (a) Douglas fir, (b) ponderosa pine, (c) western red cedar, (d) white fir.

_____

47. Fig. 9-2 is a good illustration of _____ _____.

_____

48. Check the spelling of the following words. If correct, place a "C" in the space. If incorrect, give the correct spelling.

   a. Propreties

_____

   b. Hardness

_____

   c. Sweling

_____

   d. Warping

_____

   e. Compresion

_____

   f. Toughness

_____

   g. Resistance

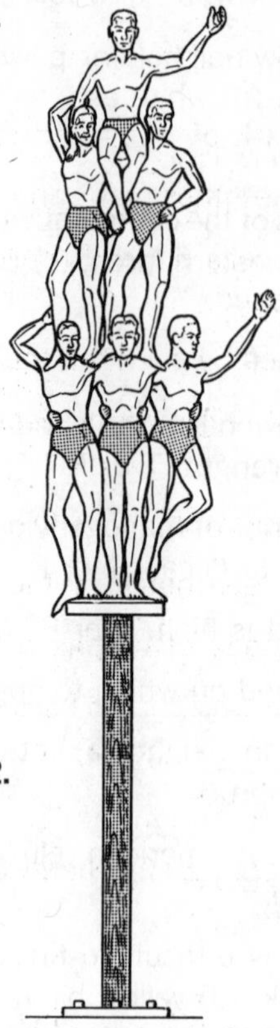

_____

Fig. 9-2.

Name_____

Score_____

Study Guide No. 10
THE NATURE OF WOOD

Reviewing the Main Ideas

1. The hard substance under the bark of trees and shrubs is _____.

2. Wood is composed of _____, like other plant and animal life.

3. The amount of moisture in wood cells depends partly on the _____ _____ to which to wood is exposed.

4. The age of a tree can be determined by counting the _____ _____.

5. The wood that is formed early in the growing season is called early or _____ wood.

6. The part of the tree just inside the cambium is the _____.

7. The grain pattern of the wood is determined by the _____ or fibers.

8. There are _____ common methods of cutting a board from a log.

9. The first method is called _____ _____ for hardwood, and _____ _____ for softwood.

10. The second method is called _____ for hardwood, and _____ _____ for softwood.

11. Softwoods are those that come from the evergreen or _____ trees.

12. Hardwoods are those cut from the _____ trees.

13. The four major chemical materials in wood are cellulose, hemicellulose, _____, and extractives.

14. The chemical derived from trees and used in clothing and rayon fiber is _____.

Checking Your Knowledge

1. Sapwood cells contain a liquid called _____.

2. Water in the cell cavities of wood is known as _____ water.

3. When both are dry, sapwood weighs considerably less than heartwood. T or F

4. The properties of wood are greatly affected when free water is removed from the cell cavities. T or F

5. As a tree grows, the heartwood increases in diameter and length. T or F

6. Identify the parts in the cross section of a tree. Fig. 10-1:

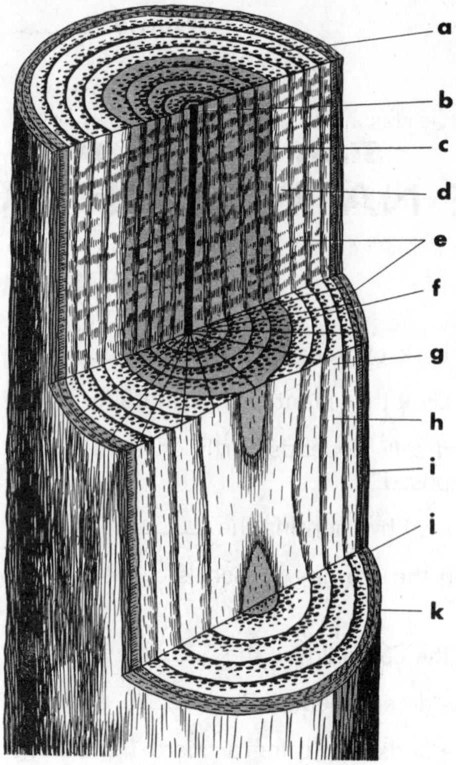

Fig. 10-1.

a. _____
b. _____
c. _____
d. _____
e. _____
f. _____
g. _____
h. _____
i. _____
j. _____
k. _____

7. The soft pitch-like material in which cell formation takes place is the _____.

8. Another name for the inner bark is bast or _____.

9. Sapwood is generally darker in color due to the presence of resin and other materials. T or F

10. The age of a tree can be determined by counting the number of growth rings. T or F

11. Growth rings are more apparent in some woods than in others. T or F

12. Another name for sapwood is _____.

13. Water in the cell walls is called _____ water.

14. When cells or fibers have grown parallel to the center of the tree, they produce a straightgrain wood. T or F

15. Plain sawed is to hardwood as _____ _____ is to softwood.

16. Quartersawed is to hardwood as _____ _____ is to softwood.

17. Plain-sawed wood does not tend to warp as much as that which is quarter-sawed. T or F

18. Softwood is to conifers as hardwood is to _____.

19. Hardwood trees shed their leaves annually. T or F

20. Oak is to quartersawed as pine is to _____ grained.

21. The age of the tree can be determined by counting the _____ rings.

22. The term "hardwood" means that the wood is very hard to cut. T or F

44

23. One of the following species is *not* classified as a hardwood: (a) birch, (b) maple, (c) oak, (d) pine.

_____

24. The heartwood is found near the outside of the tree. T or F

_____

25. Cell formation takes place in the following part of the tree: (a) pith, (b) cambium, (c) bark, (d) wood ray.

_____

26. Medullary rays are food-carrying cells that are: (a) parallel to the pith, (b) at right angles to the pitch, (c) spiral around the pith, (d) interlocked with the pith.

_____

27. The larger vertical cells of a tree are: (a) eye cells, (b) fibrils, (c) tracheids, (d) ray cells.

_____

28. Name these common leaves. Fig. 10-2:

a. _____

b. _____

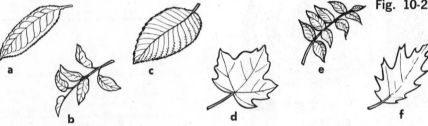

Fig. 10-2.

c. _____

d. _____

e. _____

f. _____

29. A chemical material *not* obtained from wood is: (a) cellulose, (b) hemicellulose, (c) lignin, (d) proteins.

_____

30. The average hardwood contains the following percentage of cellulose: (a) 20%, (b) 35%, (c) 45%, (d) 50%.

_____

31. The chemical "furfural" is obtained from the lignin of hardwoods. T or F

_____

32. The average softwood contains a higher percentage of lignin than the average hardwood. T or F

_____

33. Trees that shed their leaves annually are known as: (a) conifers, (b) deciduous, (c) cellulose, (d) cambium.

_____

34. Check the spelling of the following words. If correct, place a "C" in the space. If incorrect, give the correct spelling.

a. Transpiration

_____

b. Medulary

_____

c. Protoplasm

_____

d. Fiber satuation point

_____

e. Tangent

_____

f. Cellulose

_____

g. Lignen

_____

Study Guide No. 11
SEASONING

Reviewing the Main Ideas

1. The amount of water in the lumber is called the _____ _____.

2. Moisture content is given as a _____; the lower the figure, the drier the wood.

3. Lumber shrinks as it dries and swells as _____ is added.

4. As lumber dries, it does not change in size until it reaches the _____ _____ _____.

5. There is no known method for keeping _____ products absolutely free from shrinking and swelling.

6. The two common methods of drying lumber are _____ _____ and kiln drying.

7. The drying method using an oven is _____ _____.

8. Lumber must be stored properly after it is _____.

9. At any specific temperature and relative humidity, exposed wood will reach a particular _____ _____ _____.

10. Warm air can hold more _____ than cold air.

11. Inside a building, the moisture content of wood can be controlled only by controlling the _____.

12. There are two methods of checking the moisture content of wood—by the oven-drying method and with a _____ _____.

13. "Percentage of moisture content equals weight when cut minus *oven dry* weight over *oven dry* weight times 100" is the formula for the _____ method.

14. The two types of moisture meters are the needle type and the _____ type.

15. Before lumber is machined, make sure the _____ _____ is uniform and correct.

16. After a product has been built, protect the wood from great extremes of _____.

Checking Your Knowledge

1. Fungus may develop when the moisture content of wood is over 20 percent. T or F

2. When wood contains just enough water to saturate the cell walls, it is said to be at the _____ _____ _____.

3. During drying, the inner parts of the wood reduce in moisture sooner than the outer parts. T or F

_____

4. Lumber shrinks more when it is plain sawed than when it is quartersawed. T or F

_____

5. Wood shrinks about the same in length as it does in width. T or F

_____

6. Lumber that is dried out in the open is called _____ lumber.

_____

7. When seasoning rough lumber, stickers should be placed between the pieces. T or F

_____

8. When lumber has been exposed to air for an adequate length of time, the moisture content of the wood should be about _____ to _____ percent.

_____

_____

9. Kiln drying takes a longer time than air drying. T or F

_____

10. In a kiln, green one-inch lumber can be dried to about 6 to 12 percent moisture content in _____ or _____ days.

_____

_____

11. Construction lumber is usually dried to about: (a) 12 to 19%, (b) 6 to 12%, (c) 18 to 24%, (d) 4 to 8%.

_____

12. Paint will keep wood from absorbing all moisture. T or F

_____

13. There are two types of moisture meters. T or F

_____

14. The moisture meter is accurate within a range of plus or minus _____ percent.

_____

15. Top or outside pieces in a lumber pile that have been exposed to the weather may be above or below the true average of the pile. T or F

_____

16. Moisture content should be checked before lumber is machined. T or F

_____

17. If shrinkage is likely to be a serious problem, you should use plain-sawed material. T or F

_____

18. The recommended moisture content of wood for interior finishing in Nevada is _____ percent.

_____

19. The recommended moisture content of wood for interior finishing in Wisconsin is _____ percent.

_____

20. One of the following is *not* a reason for using high heat in kiln drying lumber: (a) to slow up the drying, (b) to prevent defects, (c) to remove moisture rapidly, (d) to increase rigidity.

_____

21. The method of seasoning lumber that requires the least equipment is: (a) kiln drying, (b) air drying, (c) chemical treatment, (d) summer seasoning.

_____

22. When wood is dried to a point below the fiber saturation point, it: (a) shrinks, (b) gets longer, (c) begins to decay, (d) swells.

_____

23. Wood dried to _____ percent moisture content has attained about one half its total shrinkage.

_____

24. Lumber is immune to decay after it reaches: (a) 40%, (b) 30%, (c) 25%, (d) 20% or less.   _____

25. When a board is dried rapidly in a kiln, the center will have: (a) more moisture content than the outside of the board, (b) less moisture content than the outside of the board, (c) the same moisture content as the outside, (d) no moisture content.   _____

26. If a piece of lumber weighs 14 ounces when cut and weighs 10 ounces when oven dry, the moisture content is _____ percent.   _____

27. The moisture content in Problem 26 is above the fiber saturation point. T or F   _____

28. If a piece of lumber weighs one pound when cut and weighs 13 ounces when oven dry, the moisture content is _____ percent. (Nearest whole number)   _____

29. The moisture content in Problem 28 is below the fiber saturation point. T or F   _____

30. In a very dry room, wood takes on moisture. T or F   _____

31. The freezing temperature in the metric system is 10 °C. T or F   _____

32. In the winter, the average outdoor relative humidity is _____ percent.   _____

33. Wood for furniture should be purchased dried to 8 to 10 percent. T or F   _____

34. Check the spelling of the following words. If correct, place a "C" in the space. If incorrect, give the correct spelling.

    a. Seasoning   _____

    b. Kilm dried   _____

    c. Relative humidity   _____

    d. Equilebrium   _____

    e. Shrinkage   _____

Name _____

Score _____

Study Guide No. 12
GRADING LUMBER

Reviewing the Main Ideas

1. Lumber is produced from a living and _____ material.

2. The growing material is a _____.

3. So that purchasers can know the quality of wood they buy, lumber must be divided into _____.

4. Many kinds of lumber defects affect the _____ of lumber.

5. Knots, pitch pockets, wane, and warp are some common _____.

6. There are many _____ of softwood lumber producers, each with their own grade rules.

7. Hardwood lumber is graded primarily for use in the manufacture of products such as furniture, _____, or interior house trim.

8. The best grade of hardwood lumber for furniture is _____ and _____.

9. The abbreviation S. M. in hardwood grading means _____ _____.

10. In clear face cuttings, the clear face must be on the _____ side of the board.

Checking Your Knowledge

1. Best quality lumber is found in the _____ part of the tree trunk, near the outside.

2. Pieces of higher and lower quality are found in the same grade of lumber. T or F

3. Most wood is graded while the lumber is still in the rough. T or F

4. It is easy to define the various defects found in lumber. T or F

5. A curve across the grain (width of the piece) is called _____.

6. A deviation flatwise from a straight line drawn from end to end of a piece is called _____.

7. F. A. S. means firsts and seconds. T or F

8. The clear face of the cutting shall be on the poor side of the board. T or F

9. The best grade of hardwood lumber is: (a) select seconds, (b) #1 common, (c) #2 common, (d) F. A. S.

10. Minimum width of select grade in hardwood is _____ inches.

11. Match the defects at the left to the descriptions at the right:

a. knot
b. warp
c. bark pocket
d. pitch
e. wane
f. decay
g. shake
h. check
i. stain
j. torn grain
k. skip

1. a patch of bark partly or wholly enclosed
2. a crack in wood structure
3. a disintegration of wood fibers
4. a discoloration that penetrates the wood fibers
5. a roughened area
6. an area that the planer failed to surface
7. a portion of the limb of a tree in sawed lumber
8. an accumulation of resinous material
9. presence of bark on the corners of lumber
10. any variation in a planed surface
11. a crack between annual growth rings

a. _____
b. _____
c. _____
d. _____
e. _____
f. _____
g. _____
h. _____
i. _____
j. _____
k. _____

12. The basic grading rules which all softwood lumber associations try to follow are _____ _____ _____.

_____

13. One of the following associations does *not* issue its own standards for grading softwood: (a) Redwood Inspection Service, (b) American Walnut Association, (c) Western Wood Products Association, (d) Southern Pine Inspection Service.

_____

14. Dry softwood lumber has a moisture content of: (a) 8% or less, (b) 12% or less, (c) 15% or less, (d) 19% or less.

_____

15. Lumber that is available at most lumber yards is called _____ lumber.

_____

16. Lumber used for the construction of doors, windows, and many prefabricated home items is called _____ and _____ lumber.

_____

_____

17. Softwood finish (select) grades are further classified into grades A through _____.

_____

18. The first step in grading a hardwood board for Firsts is to determine the _____ _____.

_____

19. A check defect can be described as: (a) discoloration, (b) disintegration of wood fiber, (c) a crack running lengthwise in the wood, (d) a crack between the rings of annual growth.

_____

20. Stain is considered a major defect in lumber. T or F

_____

21. The following piece of lumber would meet No. 1 Common hardwood grade. It is 3 inches wide and has 2 square feet of surface of which 75 percent can be worked into clear-face cuttings. T or F

_____

22. Surface measure means the number of _____ _____ in the board.

_____

23. One of the following is *not* a standard grade of hardwood lumber: (a) Sound Wormy, (b) Firsts, (c) Pecky, (d) No. 1 Common.

_____

24. Match the list of defects at the left to the reason for the defect at the right.
    The same number can be used several times.

    a. rot
    b. skip
    c. dote
    d. bark pocket
    e. roller check
    f. stain
    g. knot
    h. pitch
    i. machine burn
    j. wane
    k. torn grain

    1. growth defect
    2. production defect
    3. decay defect

    a. _____
    b. _____
    c. _____
    d. _____
    e. _____
    f. _____
    g. _____
    h. _____
    i. _____
    j. _____
    k. _____

25. Identify the five common kinds of knots. Fig. 12-1:

    a. _____
    b. _____
    c. _____
    d. _____
    e. _____

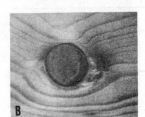
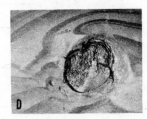

Fig. 12-1.

26. The lengths of hardwood range from: (a) 8 to 16 feet, (b) 4 to 8 feet, (c) 4 to 16 feet, (d) 10 to 16 feet.

_____

27. Green softwood lumber has a moisture content in excess of: (a) 24%, (b) 19%, (c) 28%, (d) 20%.

_____

28. Standards for softwood lumbers are available from: (a) United States Department of Commerce, (b) Bureau of Standards, (c) United States Department of Interior, (d) none of these.

_____

29. The four grades of finish lumber are: (a) No. 1, No. 2, No. 3, No. 4, (b) A select, B select, C select, and D select, (c) construction, standard, utility, and economy, (d) yard, structural, factory, and shop.

_____

30. Check the spelling of the following words. If correct, place a "C" in the space. If incorrect, give the correct spelling.

    a. Defacts   _____

    b. Associations   _____

    c. Structeral   _____

    d. Standards   _____

Name_____

Score_____

Study Guide No. 13
BUYING LUMBER

Reviewing the Main Ideas

1. Softwood logs, when cut, are grouped in three classes: _____ lumber, factory and shop lumber, and structural lumber.

_____

2. The kind of lumber usually stocked in retail yards is called _____ lumber.

_____

3. Materials usually available from a _____ lumber yard include common boards, dimension lumber, finish lumber, siding, molding, and flooring.

_____

4. In the customary system, most lumber is sold by the _____ foot.

_____

5. A piece 1 inch thick, 12 inches wide, and 12 inches long is _____ board foot.

_____

6. In ordering softwood, include the following information: quantity, size, _____, kind of wood, product, condition of seasoning, and grading rules.

_____

7. The amount of lumber delivered can be checked by using a _____ _____ rule or the Essex board measure table.

_____

8. In the metric system, a 2 x 4 has a nominal dimension of _____ x _____ millimetres.

_____

_____

9. In the metric system, thickness and width of lumber are dimensioned in _____.

_____

10. In the metric system, length of lumber is given in _____.

_____

11. The metric building module is _____ millimetres.

_____

Checking Your Knowledge

1. Lumber used for house framing is called _____ lumber.

_____

2. Identify these common kinds of siding. Fig. 13-1:

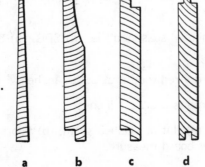

Fig. 13-1.

a   b   c   d

a. _____

b. _____

c. _____

d. _____

3. The dressed or surfaced thickness of one-inch hardwood is _____ of an inch.

4. The dressed or surfaced thickness of one-inch green pine is _____ inches.

5. A board measuring 2″ x 6″ x 12′ contains _____ board feet.

6. A 2 x 4 that is 12 feet long contains _____ board feet.

7. The letter "M" indicates _____ board feet of lumber.

8. If lumber sells for $600 per 1000 board feet, it costs _____ per board foot.

9. Identify these common patterns of molding. Fig. 13-2:

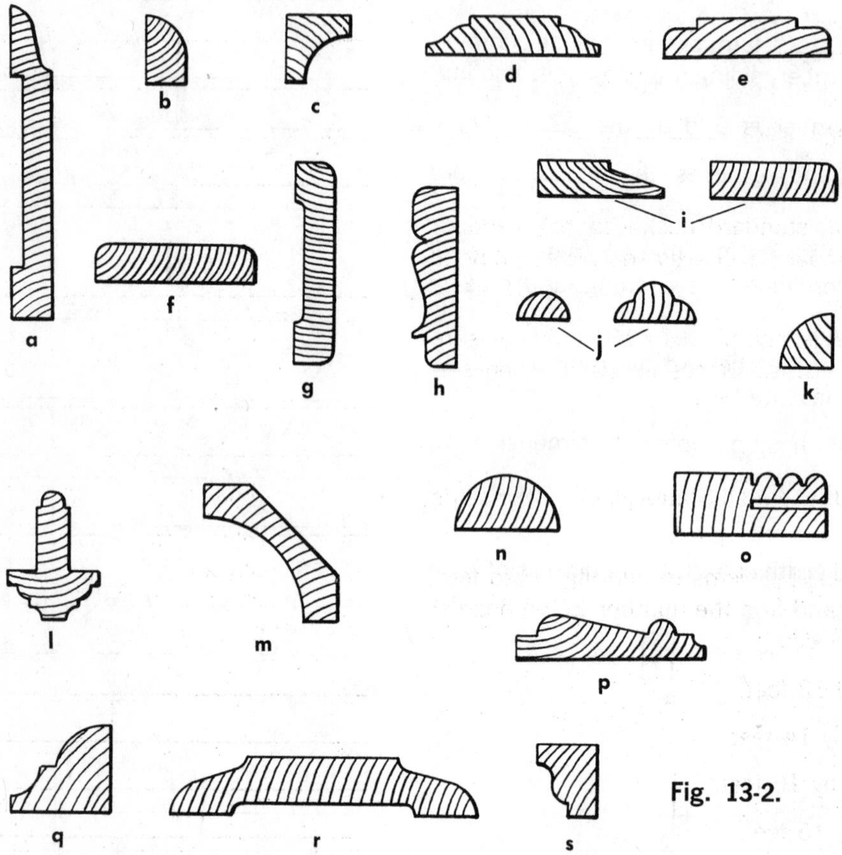

Fig. 13-2.

10. The correct lumber abbreviation for "Douglas fir" is: (a) D, (b) DF, (c) DG, (d) DE.

11. The correct lumber abbreviation for "seasoned" is: (a) SDG, (b) SD, (c) S2S, (d) SEL.

12. The dressed thickness of 3-inch dry redwood is _____ inches.

13. The S2S thickness of 3-inch walnut is _____ inches.

14. The abbreviation FLG indicates: (a) flat or slashed grain, (b) flooring, (c) feet surface measure, (d) feet board measure.

a. _____
b. _____
c. _____
d. _____
e. _____
f. _____
g. _____
h. _____
i. _____
j. _____
k. _____
l. _____
m. _____
n. _____
o. _____
p. _____
q. _____
r. _____
s. _____

15. Identify these commonly used lumber abbreviations:

    a. AD

    b. KD

    c. S2S

    d. WTH

    e. FT

    f. M

    g. RGH

    h. DIM

    i. FLG

16. Standard lengths of softwood range from _____ to _____ feet.

17. Hardwood lumber is available in: (a) standard thickness, (b) standard thickness, width, and length, (c) standard thickness and width, (d) none of these.

18. A piece of dry dimension lumber that is a nominal 4 x 10 would measure _____ inches in thickness and _____ inches in width, when surfaced.

19. Lumber yards in different parts of the United States all carry the same species of softwoods. T or F

20. The following are some mathematical problems in figuring board feet. Use any of the rules for board feet and find the number to the nearest even board foot for the following pieces:

    a. 10 pieces 1 inch by 3 inches by 12 feet.

    b. 18 pieces 1 inch by 10 inches by 14 feet.

    c. 24 pieces 2 inches by 4 inches by 16 feet.

    d. 30 pieces 1 inch by 3 inches by 16 feet.

    e. 6 pieces 1 inch by 12 inches by 14 feet.

    f. 9 pieces 1 inch by 6 inches by 14 inches.

    g. 3 pieces 1 inch by 10 inches by 14 feet.

21. Another name for a board rule is the _____ _____ stick.

22. The Essex board measure table can be found on: (a) a special table, (b) try square, (c) framing or rafter square, (d) combination square.

23. Dimension lumber varies in thickness from: (a) 2 to 5 inches, (b) 3 to 6 inches, (c) 2 to 6 inches, (d) 2 to 8 inches.

24. The surfaced or dressed thickness of a one-inch piece of softwood is the same as a one-inch piece of hardwood. T or F

_____

25. Find the total number of board feet in the following piles of lumber:

a. 2 pieces of 1 1/2'' lumber—each piece is 10 board measure; 3 pieces of 1'' lumber—each piece is 15 board measure; 5 pieces of 2'' lumber—each piece is 18 board measure.

_____

b. 3 pieces of 2'' lumber—each piece is 15 board measure; 5 pieces of 1 3/4'' lumber—each piece is 9 board measure; 12 pieces of 1'' lumber—each piece is 14 board measure.

_____

26. A 100 millimetre module equals about 4 inches. T or F

_____

27. Metric lengths of lumber begin at _____ metres.

_____

28. When the 100 millimetre building module is used, panel stock will measure _____ by _____ millimetres.

_____

_____

29. Check the spelling of the following words. If correct, place a "C" in the space. If incorrect, give the correct spelling.

a. Dimensien

_____

b. Flooring

_____

c. Surfaced

_____

d. Nominial

_____

Study Guide No. 14
PLYWOOD AND VENEERS

Reviewing the Main Ideas

1. Plywood is a glued-up panel consisting of layers or _____ of veneer, or veneer and solid wood.

   _____

2. Plywood consists of a _____, crossbands, and faces.

   _____

3. A thin sheet of wood that is sawed, peeled, or sliced from a log is called _____.

   _____

4. Two kinds of hardwood plywood are _____ core plywood, and lumber core plywood.

   _____

5. A giant lathe or a slicer is used to cut _____.

   _____

6. The three methods of cutting veneer are: rotary cutting, _____ slicing, and quarter slicing.

   _____

7. Modern hardwood plywood for furniture can be described as a marriage between aesthetics and _____.

   _____

8. Furniture manufacturers make their own _____ core plywood.

   _____

9. Plywood has the advantages of being _____, retaining its dimensions, having a smooth surface, and being easy to bend.

   _____

10. The advantage of veneer applied to particle board is greater _____ stability.

    _____

11. The grade standards for _____ plywood include information on the faces and backs, types, dimensions, thickness, and core construction.

    _____

12. Panels formerly called softwood plywood are now indicated as _____ and industrial plywood.

    _____

13. Most construction and industrial plywood is made from _____ _____.

    _____

14. In plywood construction, the number of _____ may be an even number but the number of _____ is always an odd number.

    _____

    _____

15. Grades of construction and industrial plywood are indicated by _____.

Checking Your Knowledge

1. One of the following is *not* a basic layer, or ply, of plywood: (a) faces, (b) cores, (c) flitches, (d) crossbands.

   _____

2. A thin sheet of wood that is sawed, peeled, or sliced from a log is called _____.

   _____

3. There are two types of hardwood plywoods, namely, _____ core and _____ core.

4. Identify these three methods of cutting plywood veneer. Fig. 14-1:

a. _____

b. _____

c. _____

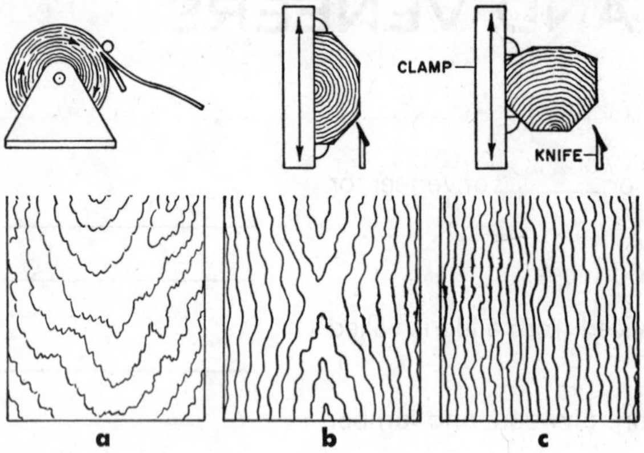

CLAMP

KNIFE

Fig. 14-1.

a   b   c

5. The most costly method of veneer cutting is _____ _____.

6. All logs or flitches must be softened or tenderized before cutting the veneer. T or F

7. A three-ply, 3/8-inch (9.5 mm) panel has better strength and shrinkage properties than a five-ply, 3/8-inch (9.5 mm) panel. T or F

8. Common lumbers for the core of lumber core plywood are _____ and _____.

9. The standard American face veneer is _____ (millimetres) in thickness.

10. The veneer imported from many countries is 1/60th of an inch (0.42 mm). T or F

11. Veneering in the school shop can be done over plywood. T or F

12. Veneer is sold by the _____ foot.

13. Plywood, weight for weight, is always stronger than solid wood. T or F

14. The best face and back grade of hardwood plywood is _____ grade.

15. The poorest face and back grade of hardwood plywood is: (a) good grade, (b) sound grade, (c) utility grade, (d) backing grade.

16. Type II hardwood plywood has a weather-resistant bond. T or F

17. Five-ply hardwood veneer core plywood is *not* available in one of the following thicknesses: (a) 1/4″ (6.4 mm), (b) 5/16″ (7.9 mm), (c) 3/8″ (9.5 mm), (d) 1/2″ (12.7 mm).

18. Three-quarter-inch (19 mm) hardwood plywood is available with _____ and _____ plies.

19. Furniture built-ins and other fixtures, where edge treatment is desired, usually require _____ _____ plywood.

60

20. Veneer core plywood is best used for bending and for exterior purposes. T or F

_____

21. The strongest woods used in construction and industrial plywood are in Group _____.

_____

22. The best grade face of construction and industrial plywood is _____.

_____

23. The lowest grade of construction and industrial plywood is given the letter _____.

_____

24. Identify the following uses of plywood. Fig. 14-2:

1. _____
2. _____
3. _____
4. _____
5. _____
6. _____
7. _____
8. _____
9. _____
10. _____

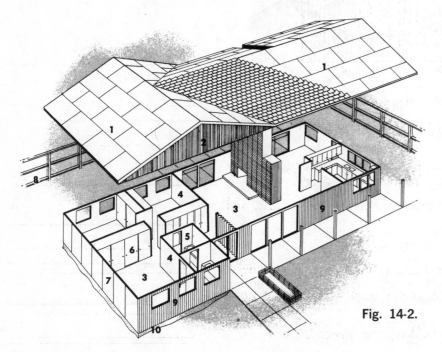

Fig. 14-2.

25. The best method of storing plywood is to place it on edge. T or F

_____

26. When using a portable hand power saw, always put the good side face up. T or F

_____

27. The correct size screw to use for 3/4-inch (19 mm) plywood is _____.

_____

28. The best joint for plywood corners is a _____ joint.

_____

29. The best adhesive to use in a school shop for applying veneer to full plywood or hardboard is: (a) resin glue, (b) contact cement, (c) animal glue, (d) epoxy resin.

_____

30. Exterior type construction and industrial plywood of grade A-A has inner plies of grade _____.

_____

31. Interior type construction and industrial plywood of grade A-B has inner plies of grade _____.

_____

32. The method of matching veneers shown in the text in Fig. 14-14a is _____ _____.

_____

33. Identify the parts of this lumber core plywood door. Fig. 14-3:

Fig. 14-3.

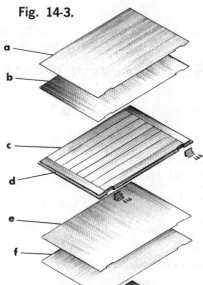
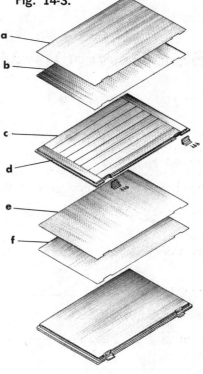

a. _____

b. _____

c. _____

d. _____

e. _____

f. _____

34. A very common size of plywood is 4' width x 8' length (1220 x 2440 mm). T or F

_____

35. The most common method of cutting veneer is: (a) flat sliced, (b) quarter sliced, (c) rotary sliced, (d) angle sliced.

36. The standard thickness in inches of American face veneer is: (a) 1/32, (b) 1/28, (c) 1/8, (d) 1/16.

_____

37. Logs for veneers are put through hot water or a steam bath for the following purpose: (a) to give uniform color, (b) to soften or tenderize, (c) to prevent warping, (d) to remove the sap.

_____

38. In hardwood plywood, a fully waterproof bond is called: (a) Type I, (b) Type A, (c) Type II, (d) Type III.

_____

39. Group 5 species used for construction and industrial plywood do *not* include: (a) basswood, (b) fire, balsam, (c) birch, (d) poplar, balsam.

_____

40. One of the following is *not* a major type of construction and industrial plywood: (a) exterior, (b) bonded, (c) structural, (d) interior.

_____

41. A flat-roof building measures 20' x 40' and has an 8' ceiling. Give the number of 4' x 8' (1220 x 2400 mm) plywood sheets needed to cover the exterior walls.

_____

42. Figure how many hardwood plywood doors measuring 12" x 16" can be cut from a sheet of plywood that measures 48" x 96" (1220 x 2440 mm).

_____

43. Check the spelling of the following words. If correct, place a "C" in the space. If incorrect, give the correct spelling.

a. Species

_____

b. Roteary

_____

c. Venearing

_____

d. Plywood

_____

e. Exterier

_____

Study Guide No. 15
PROCESSED WOOD MATERIALS

Reviewing the Main Ideas

1. Hardboard and particle board are two _____ materials that make use of wood fibers, chips, and shavings.

2. The first two steps in the manufacture of _____ are to reduce the wood to uniform chips and then change the chips to individual wood fibers.

3. Next, _____ are refined and made into a board by compression under heat and pressure.

4. Hardboard is made in five types, standard, _____, service, service-tempered, and industrialite.

5. Hardboards are made with many special decorative _____.

6. Production machining of hardboard is done with _____ tools.

7. Particle board is a combination of _____ and wood chips, scraps, flakes, or other wood fragments.

8. Particle board is a relatively new _____ material.

9. Particle board is made by pressing the mixture of wood _____ and adhesives together in a hot press to form the board.

10. The physical properties of particle board vary greatly with the kind of wood used, the kind and amount of _____, and the pressure.

11. Plastic laminates are attached to particle board cores with _____ cement.

12. Sheetboard, or ply-veneer, is made from low-grade lumber and _____ paper.

13. Insulation board is a low-density board made from fibers of _____, cane, and other vegetable matter.

14. A light core material covered with facings of stiff, sturdy material is called _____ construction.

Checking Your Knowledge

1. Hardboard is an all-wood panel manufactured from wood fibers. T or F

2. One of the following is *not* a characteristic of hardboard: (a) exceptional strength, (b) superior wear resistance, (c) hard to work with ordinary tools, (d) easy to paint.

3. There are two classes of standard hardboards. T or F

4. Tempered or treated hardboard is not as strong as standard hardboard. T or F

5. Hardboard identified as S1S has one smooth surface and one rough surface that looks like screening. T or F

6. When quantity production of hardboard products is done, it is better to use tools with _____ cutting edges.

7. When cutting hardboard, the exposed surface should be up. T or F

8. Nails for interior hardboard should be 3d _____ finishing nails.

9. Hardboard can be toenailed. T or F

10. Particle board is real wood in a _____ form.

11. When nailing hardboard, never nail closer than _____ of an inch to the edge.

12. Particle board is one of the results of modern research in wood technology. T or F

13. One of the following is *not* a common wood used in making particle board: (a) poplar, (b) pine, (c) hemlock, (d) walnut.

14. The most common panel sizes of particle board are 4' x 8' (1220 x 2440 mm) and _____ x _____ (feet).

15. The physical properties of all particle board are identical. T or F

16. Particle board can be worked with standard wood tools. T or F

17. Hardboard on which both surfaces are very smooth is indicated by the following symbol: (a) S1S, (b) S2S, (c) HAS, (d) S4S.

18. A compound bend can be made in hardboard. T or F

19. All classes of hardboards are manufactured with two types of surfaces. T or F

20. Forcing bulk material through small openings is called _____.

21. Tempered or treated hardboard is known as: (a) Type I, (b) Type II, (c) Type A, (d) Type B.

22. The manufacture of particle board has developed largely since: (a) 1910, (b) 1915, (c) 1926, (d) 1948.

23. In some types of particle board there are larger chips near the center and smaller ones toward the surface. T or F

24. The grain direction of particle board is from end to end. T or F

25. Sheetboard is a sheathing product made of low-grade lumber glued to a wet-strength kraft paper. T or F

26. Two common names for insulation board are _____ and _____.

27. Insulation board is a high-density hardboard. T or F

28. Sound-absorbing structural insulation board is called _____ board.

29. Sandwich construction is layer construction made by bonding thin facings to a thick core. T or F

30. Insulation board is harder and of higher density than hardboard. T or F   _____

31. Check the spelling of the following words. If correct, place a "C" in the space. If incorrect, give the correct spelling.

    a. Hardboard   _____

    b. Tempered   _____

    c. Texteur   _____

    d. Particle board   _____

    e. Extrucion   _____

    f. Acustical   _____

Study Guide No. 16
OTHER CONSTRUCTION MATERIALS

Reviewing the Main Ideas

1. The principal competitors of wood include ceramics, steel, _____, and plastics.

2. Ceramic materials are hard, strong, and _____.

3. Steel and cast iron are made primarily of iron and are called _____ materials.

4. The major drawback of mild steel is that it is heavy and it _____.

5. The most common nonferrous material used in home construction is _____.

6. Aluminum is a poor conductor of _____ heat.

7. The main ingredients of plastics are carbon, oxygen, hydrogen, and _____.

8. Plastics do not consist of a single material but, rather, are a _____ of materials.

9. At some stage in manufacture, plastics are always in a _____ state.

10. Plastics, because of good heat insulating properties, are used for _____ in the home.

11. Because plastics have a petroleum base, they _____ more than traditional materials.

12. Almost all adhesives and protective coatings contain some _____.

Checking Your Knowledge

1. There is no material used in construction that is superior to wood. T or F

2. One of the following is *not* a ceramic material: (a) brick and stone, (b) cement and concrete, (c) glass, (d) fiberglass.

3. One of the following is *not* a characteristic of ceramic materials: (a) good heat conductors, (b) hard, (c) brittle, (d) nonresilient.

4. A disadvantage of ceramic materials is that they are expensive. T or F

5. Ceramic materials usually require some kind of reinforcing. T or F

6. One of the following is *not* a characteristic of mild steel: (a) it is heavy, (b) it is non-corrosive, (c) it rusts, (d) it does not burn.

7. Steel is not susceptible to fire. T or F

8. One principal use of aluminum is for windows. T or F

9. One of the following is *not* true of aluminum: (a) it can be shaped into many building components, (b) it is growing in popularity as a building material, (c) it contains a high percentage of iron, (d) it is considered nonferrous.

_____

10. One of the following is *not* a characteristic of aluminum: (a) it does not dent, (b) it is light in weight, (c) it is durable, (d) it is a good reflector.

_____

11. Aluminum windows help to keep down fuel bills. T or F

_____

12. In their finished state, plastics are solid. T or F

_____

13. One of the following does *not* apply to plastics: (a) tough, (b) easy to form, (c) good insulators, (d) fairly heavy.

_____

14. Plastics maintain a good appearance when used out of doors. T or F

_____

15. Plastics are difficult to color. T or F

_____

16. Of the following, the most costly building material is: (a) wood, (b) steel, (c) plastics, (d) concrete.

_____

17. Plastics are extremely strong and rigid. T or F

_____

18. Plastics are highly resistant to fire and heat. T or F

_____

19. Plastics are *not* commonly found in one of the following materials: (a) concrete block, (b) adhesives, (c) hardboard, (d) particle board.

_____

20. Plastics which soften when heated are called _____.

_____

21. Plastics which cannot be reshaped are called _____.

_____

22. Match the plastics at the left to the descriptions at the right:

   a. acrylic   1. good for use out of doors
   b. vinyl   2. commonly used for skylights
   c. polyethylene   3. becomes soft and flexible when heated

a. _____

b. _____

c. _____

23. One of the following is *not* a thermosetting plastic: (a) melamine-amino, (b) polyester, (c) polyvinyl, (d) phenolic.

_____

24. The most common plastics for home and furniture construction are _____ and _____.

_____

25. In its liquid state, _____ is used to coat such products as boats and water skis.

_____

26. One of the following is *not* a characteristic of plastic laminates: (a) great strength, (b) decorative, (c) available in many colors, (d) can imitate wood grain.

_____

27. The standard thickness of plastic laminate is: (a) 1/8″ (3.2 mm), (b) 1/32″ (0.8 mm), (c) 1/16″ (1.6 mm), (d) 1/4″ (6.4 mm).

_____

28. It is a good idea to use carbide-tipped tools when cutting plastic laminate. T or F

_____

29. The correct adhesive for applying plastic laminates is: (a) hide glue, (b) fish glue, (c) animal glue, (d) contact cement.

_____

30. Plastic laminates should be applied at a temperature of _____ (degrees Fahrenheit) or above.

_____

31. Plastic laminates can be bent without heat to a radius of: (a) 8″ (203.2 mm), (b) 11″ (279.4 mm), (c) 9″ (228.6 mm), (d) 10″ (254.0 mm).

_____

32. When heated, plastic laminate can be bent to a radius of _____ (millimetres).

_____

33. An electric-powered router saves much time in trimming the edges of plastic laminates. T or F

_____

34. Check the spelling of the following words. If correct, place a "C" in the space. If incorrect, give the correct spelling.

   a. Ceramic

_____

   b. Alumunin

_____

   c. Flamability

_____

   d. Polyvinyl

_____

   e. Polyeithilene

_____

   f. Phenolic

_____

   g. Polester

_____

Study Guide No. 17
WOOD SCIENCE

Reviewing the Main Ideas

1. Wood science is a study of the physical and _____ properties of wood.

2. Wood can be identified by color, odor, weight, hardness, and _____.

3. Wood can be cut in _____ distinct planes with respect to the annular rings.

4. Hardwoods are called porous woods and conifers are called _____ woods.

5. Medullary rays, also known as _____ rays, are narrow bands of cells extending radially in a tree.

6. Conifers differ in structure from hardwoods because conifers have no _____ and no true _____ _____.

7. The woods of pines, spruce, larch, and Douglas fir contain _____ ducts.

8. A simple way of determining the specific gravity of a piece of wood is by the _____ method.

Checking Your Knowledge

1. Color is a reliable means for identification of wood. T or F

2. A microscope usually enlarges cell structures from 70 to _____ times.

3. One of the following is an open-grained wood: (a) beech, (b) oak, (c) maple, (d) basswood.

4. Pith flecks are abnormal groups of wood cells appearing at the end of some woods. T or F

5. Tracheids are elongated cells found in all hardwoods. T or F

6. One of the following is *not* a resinous softwood: (a) Douglas fir, (b) white pine, (c) red cedar, (d) western larch.

7. One of the following woods does *not* have resin ducts: (a) Douglas fir, (b) larch, (c) spruce, (d) walnut.

8. When the weights of various woods are compared, the woods must all be at the same stage of dryness. T or F

9. For oven drying of wood, the oven must maintain a constant temperature of _____ to _____ (degrees Celsius).

10. Check the spelling of the following words. If correct, place a "C" in the space. If incorrect, give the correct spelling.

a. Transverse   _____

b. Trachieds   _____

c. Parenchyma   _____

d. Tiloses   _____

Name_____

Score_____

Study Guide No. 18
MODIFIED WOODS AND WOOD PRESERVATIVES

Reviewing the Main Ideas

1. Wood shrinks as it loses _____.

2. The abbreviation for polyethylene glycol-1000 is _____.

3. Wood is low in dimensional stability as compared to _____.

4. Polyethylene glycol-1000 treatment does not affect the odor or _____ of wood.

5. The abbreviation for wood-plastic composites is _____.

6. In industry, wood-plastic composites are cured by exposure to _____ from gamma sources.

7. Wood preservatives are used to protect against insects or _____.

8. To protect wood, the best method of applying materials is by _____.

9. The two methods of applying fire-retardant solutions is by pressure or in the _____ used.

Checking Your Knowledge

1. One of the following does *not* take place as wood takes on and loses moisture: (a) the wood changes in strength, (b) the wood cracks, (c) it warps, (d) it splits.

2. Polyethylene glycol-1000 has the following effect on wood: (a) protects it against insects, (b) protects it against dotting, (c) prevents moisture absorption, (d) helps wood to resist change in dimension.

3. Wood treated with polyethylene glycol-1000 takes paint better than untreated wood. T or F

4. One of the following kinds of containers should *not* be used for treating wood: (a) plastic, (b) metal, (c) glass, (d) earthenware.

5. The drier wood is, the better it absorbs wood treatment. T or F

6. The length of time required to treat wood is the same for all species. T or F

7. One of the following is *not* an effect that wood-plastic composites have on wood: (a) making it more durable, (b) making it chip more easily, (c) with dyes, making it a more even color throughout, (d) beautifying it.

8. Wood-plastic products require a varnish finish. T or F

9. One of the following is *not* a characteristic of wood-plastic composites: (a) can burn or explode, (b) can cause throat irritation, (c) must be stored in a cool, dark place, (d) have no odor to warn the worker.

10. Wood-plastic composites work best on green wood. T or F

11. One of the following is *not* a less expensive wood commonly treated with wood-plastic composites: (a) walnut, (b) soft maple, (c) cottonwood, (d) basswood.

12. Treated wood should be cured by exposure to the air. T or F

13. It takes ———— hours to cure treated wood.

14. Dyes used to color wood-plastic composites must be soluble in oil. T or F

15. Pigments make a good colorant for treated woods. T or F

16. Glues that work best with wood-plastic composites are epoxy resin or ————.

17. To obtain a good glued joint on wood-plastic composites, no clamping is necessary. T or F

18. Materials made of wood-plastic composites can be machined about the same as untreated wood. T or F

19. Materials made from wood-plastic composites do *not* have one of the following working qualities: (a) can be buffed to higher luster than untreated wood, (b) surface can be darkened by application of oil or wax, (c) can take a good varnish finish, (d) cannot be finished for use with food.

20. The best prevention against rotting and insects is applied by: (a) chemicals with pressure, (b) spraying, (c) dipping, (d) brushing.

21. Match the wood preservatives at the left to the descriptions at the right:

    a. water-borne
    b. creosote
    c. oil-borne

    1. good when wood is to be used in the ground
    2. good for buildings that will stand above ground
    3. good for wood that is to be painted

    a. ————
    b. ————
    c. ————

22. Wood has better resistance to fire than many non-combustible materials. T or F

23. Fire retardants must penetrate wood fibers to be effective. T or F

24. Check the spelling of the following words. If correct, place a "C" after the word. If incorrect, give the correct spelling.

    a. Glycall

    b. Stabylized

    c. Monnomers

    d. Polymerization

    e. Creosote

Name _____

Score _____

Study Guide No. 19
WOOD FLOUR MOLDING

Reviewing the Main Ideas

1. Wood flour is sized by air screening or _____ methods.

2. Wood flour is used in combination with various plastic resins in the form of _____.

3. Wood waste is often used as a feed for _____.

4. To produce products of wood flour, it is necessary to have a _____ press.

5. The devices to shape and size products are called _____.

6. To color the products made by flour molding, use powdered _____.

7. In addition to pressure, it is necessary to apply _____.

Checking Your Knowledge

1. Wood flour is *not* used to produce one of the following: (a) particle board, (b) toys, (c) furniture parts, (d) tool handles.

2. The size of wood flour products is determined by the size of the _____ _____.

3. Special glass containers are needed for mixing wood flour in the shop. T or F

4. Wood flour should have a uniform texture which is produced by _____.

5. The plastic resins mixed with wood flour must be the dry type. T or F

6. Coloring added to wood flour should be in the form of liquid pigment. T or F

7. One of the following is *not* used to make the molds for forming products of wood flour: (a) cold-rolled steel, (b) aluminum, (c) hardwood, (d) cast iron.

8. A release must be applied to the interior of the mold before it is heated. T or F

9. Check the spelling of the following words. If correct, place a "C" in the space. If incorrect, give the correct spelling.

   a. Hydraulic

   b. Dye

   c. Adhecives

   d. Melamine

Study Guide No. 20
MATERIAL AND STRUCTURAL TESTING

Reviewing the Main Ideas

1. Wood, metal, and _____ are the three major materials used in manu-facturing and construction.

2. Wood is light in weight, yet pound for pound stiffer and stronger than _____ _____.

3. The forces acting on a piece of material and tending to change its shape are called _____.

4. Deformation in a part caused by applying load or force is called _____.

5. Loads can be classified as either dead or _____.

6. Loads applied a large number of times are called repeated or _____ loads.

7. The greatest stress that a material is capable of developing without retaining permanent change in size or shape after the load is removed is called the _____ _____.

8. When the proportional limit is exceeded, the wood fails completely and a _____ _____ occurs.

9. _____ is the property that makes the surface of a timber resist denting and scratching.

10. The most rigid geometric shape used in construction is the _____.

Checking Your Knowledge

1. One of the following is *not* a physical property of wood: (a) dimensions, (b) density, (c) hardness, (d) moisture content.

2. One of the following is *not* a mechanical property of wood: (a) stiffness, (b) sound reflection, (c) bending strength, (d) hardness.

3. One of the following is *not* a common kind of stress: (a) tensile, (b) strain, (c) compressive, (d) shear.

4. Wood is used in many types of construction which require high tensile strength. T or F

5. The measure of the ability to carry loads along the length of wood is called _____ strength.

6. As a load or force is applied to a piece of wood, the size and shape of the material is always changed, at least slightly. T or F

7. One of the following is *not* a kind of live load: (a) static, (b) repeated, (c) deflected, (d) impact.

8. The measure of stiffness of a material or the measure of resistance to deflection is: (a) modulus of elasticity, (b) proportional limit, (c) deflection, (d) breaking strength.

9. Knots on short compression pieces reduce the strength directly in proportion to the knot size. T or F

10. A joist that is 10 inches deep is about _____ as stiff as one of equal width and quality but only 8 inches deep.

11. A commercial machine used for making mechanical tests on wood and wood products is called a _____ _____ machine.

12. Floor joists used in house construction should be high in _____ and have good bending strength.

13. Standard test data for plastic laminates have been established by the National Electrical Manufacturers Association. T or F

14. The most basic geometric shape used for adding strength in furniture construction is the: (a) rectangle, (b) hexagon, (c) triangle, (d) square.

15. Check the spelling of the following words. If correct, place a "C" in the space. If incorrect, give the correct spelling.

    a. Reserch

    b. Experrmentation

    c. Thermel

    d. Tencile

    e. Deflecetion

    f. Modulus

Name_____

Score_____

Study Guide No. 21
WOOD IN OUR ENVIRONMENT

Reviewing the Main Ideas

1. One of the nation's few renewable resources is _____. _____

2. The amount of forest lands in metric terms equals _____ hectares. _____

3. One advantage of wood as a building material is that it requires less _____ to produce. _____

4. Two types of forest lands used for recreation are national forests and _____ lands. _____

5. Trees conserve carbon dioxide and release _____ as they grow. _____

6. The least desirable way to use a tree in the product cycle is to _____ it. _____

7. The first major use for forests is as _____ areas. _____

8. Each American generates about 7 pounds (3.2 kg) of waste a day, of which _____ is in the form of paper products. _____

Checking Your Knowledge

1. Forest products are decreasing in supply. T or F _____

2. Forest lands in the United States total in acres about: (a) 80 million, (b) 8 million, (c) 800 million, (d) 8 billion. _____

3. More than 50 percent of our timber is on federal land. T or F _____

4. One of the following is *not* a characteristic of wood as a building material: (a) the supply can be controlled, (b) it does not have to be imported, (c) less energy is required to produce it, (d) the rate of growth remains the same. _____

5. Match the forest lands at the left to the number of acres they comprise at the right:

   a. developed acres
   b. timberland that can be commercially harvested
   c. privately owned forest land
   d. holdings of forest-industry enterprises

   1. 360 million acres
   2. 65 million acres
   3. 100 000 acres
   4. 500 million acres

   a. _____
   b. _____
   c. _____
   d. _____

6. One of the following is *not* among ways that trees help to clean the air: (a) by changing oxygen to carbon dioxide, (b) by changing carbon dioxide to oxygen, (c) by filtering impurities from the air, (d) by reducing the amount of foreign substances in the air. _____

7. One of the following is *not* a way in which trees affect our environment: (a) by acting as a screen against bright sunlight, (b) by increasing the need for electrical energy, (c) by reducing noise, (d) by controlling water runoff during rainstorms.

_____

8. Every part of a tree can be used except the bark. T or F

_____

9. Number the following in the best order for full utilization of a tree:

   Logs for a fireplace

_____

   Building materials for a home

_____

   Left standing in a recreational area

_____

   Wood to be used for building furniture

_____

   Production of food and chemicals

_____

10. When comparing all our natural resources in terms of their benefits to people, wood ranks: (a) No. 4, (b) No. 3, (c) No. 2, (d) No. 1.

_____

11. Solid fiber wasted every year adds up to millions of tons. T or F

_____

12. Most fiber waste is in the form of: (a) sawdust, (b) wood chips, (c) paper, (d) wood flour.

_____

13. Solid waste fiber cannot be recycled. T or F

_____

14. Check the spelling of the following words. If correct, place a "C" in the space. If incorrect, give the correct spelling.

   a. Renuwable

_____

   b. Hectares

_____

   c. Petroleom

_____

   d. Environmental

_____

   e. Procesing

_____

Section D—Unit 22
Pages 298–301

Name ______________________________

Score ____________

Study Guide No. 22

LAYOUT, MEASURING, AND CHECKING DEVICES

Checking Your Knowledge

1. Fig. 22-1

   Name ______________________________

   Uses ______________________________

   ____

   ____

   ____

   ____

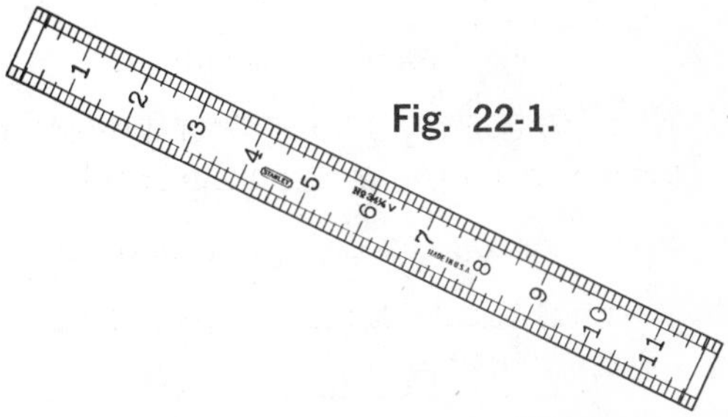

Fig. 22-1.

2. Fig. 22-2

   Name ______________________________

   Uses ______________________________

   ____

   ____

   ____

   ____

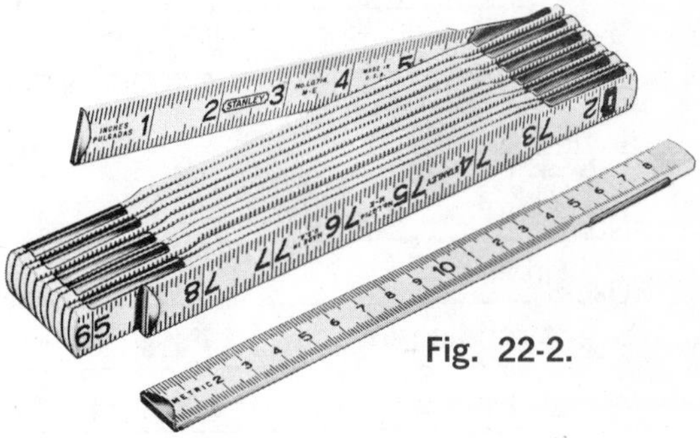

Fig. 22-2.

3. Fig. 22-3

   Name ______________________________

   Uses ______________________________

   ____

   ____

   ____

   ____

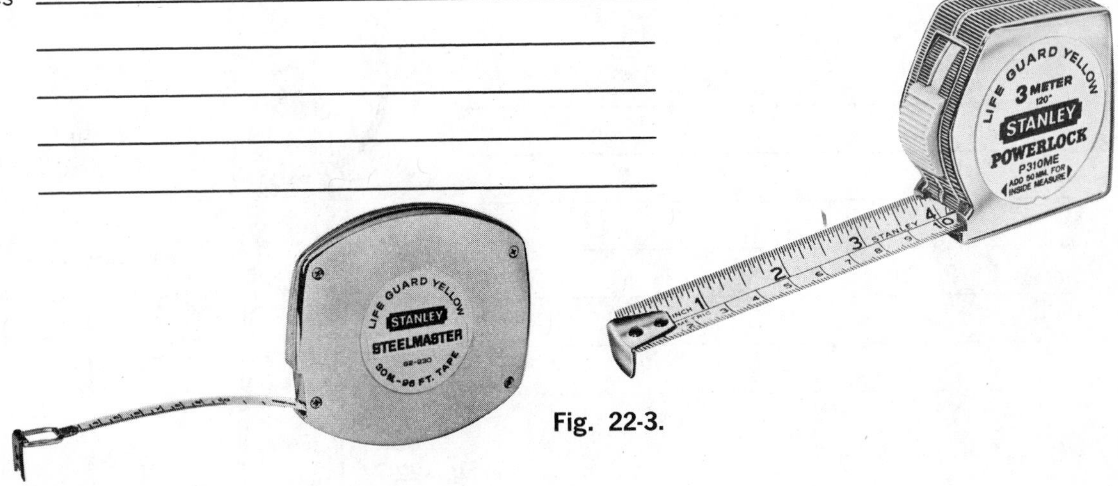

Fig. 22-3.

4. Fig. 22-4

   Name _____

   Uses _____

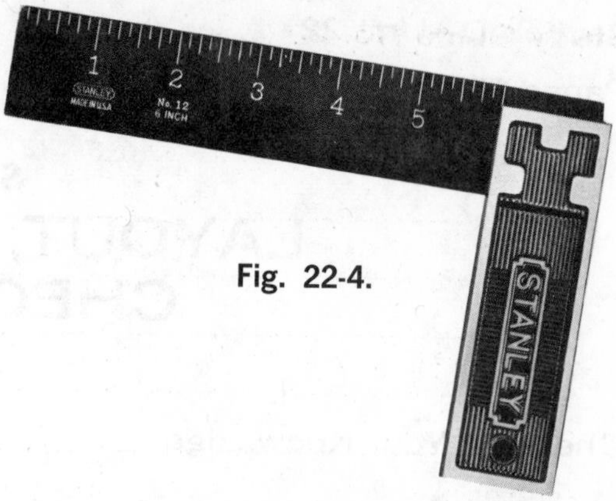

   _____

   _____

   _____

   _____

   _____

Fig. 22-4.

5. Fig. 22-5

   Name _____

   Uses _____

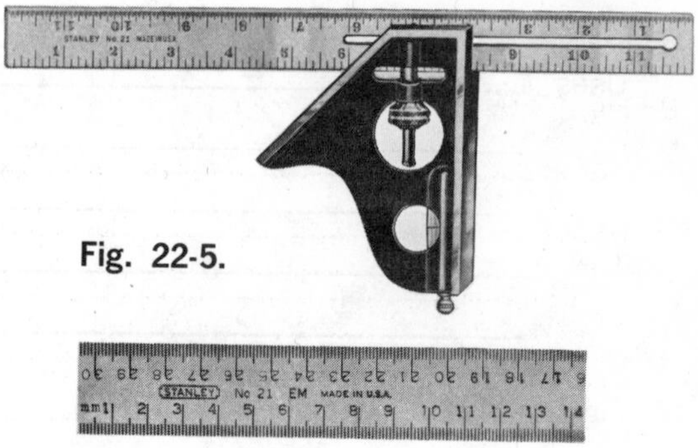

   _____

   _____

   _____

   _____

   _____

Fig. 22-5.

6. Fig. 22-6

   Name _____

   Uses _____

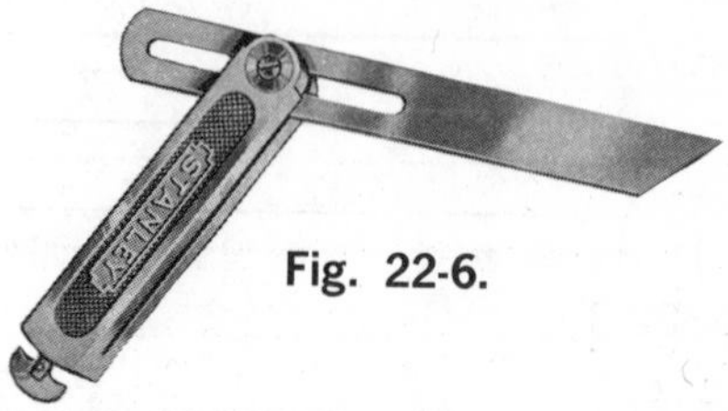

   _____

   _____

   _____

   _____

   _____

Fig. 22-6.

7. Fig. 22-7

   Name _____

   Uses _____

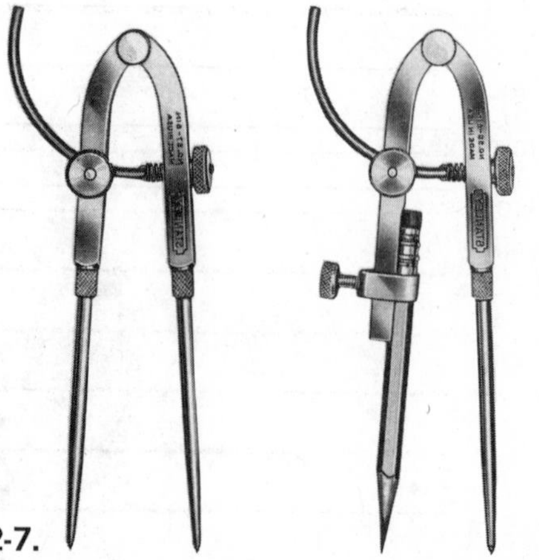

   _____

   _____

   _____

   _____

   _____

Fig. 22-7.

8. Fig. 22-8

    Name _____

    Uses _____

    _____

    _____

    _____

    _____

    _____

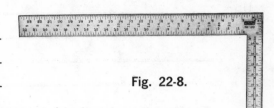

Fig. 22-8.

9. Fig. 22-9

    Name _____

    Uses _____

    _____

    _____

    _____

    _____

    _____

    _____

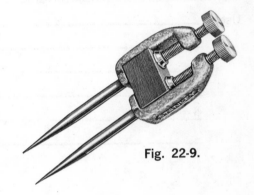

Fig. 22-9.

10. Fig. 22-10

    Name _____

    Use _____

    _____

    _____

    _____

    _____

Fig. 22-10.

11. Fig. 22-11

    Name _____

    Uses _____

    _____

    _____

    _____

    _____

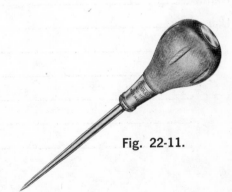

Fig. 22-11.

12. Fig. 22-12

Name _____

Use _____

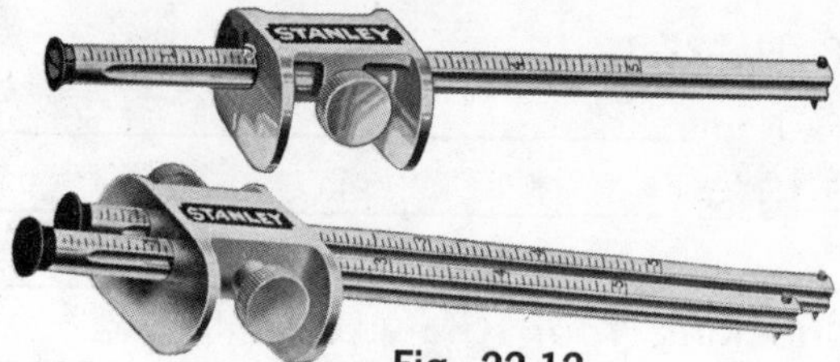

_____

_____

_____

_____

_____

Fig. 22-12.

13. Fig. 22-13

Name _____

Uses _____

_____

_____

_____

_____

_____

Fig. 22-13.

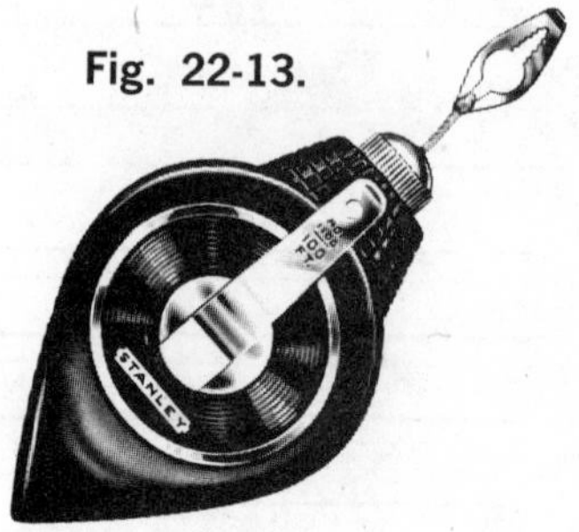

Section D—Unit 23 Name ______________________________

Pages 302–304 Score __________

Study Guide No. 23

SAWING TOOLS

Checking Your Knowledge

1. Fig. 23-1

   Name ______________________________

   Uses ______________________________

   ____

   ____

   ____

   ____

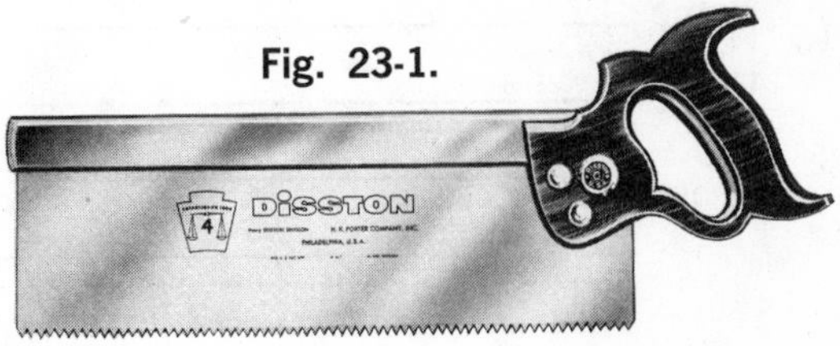

Fig. 23-1.

2. Fig. 23-2

   Name ______________________________

   Uses ______________________________

   ____

   ____

   ____

   ____

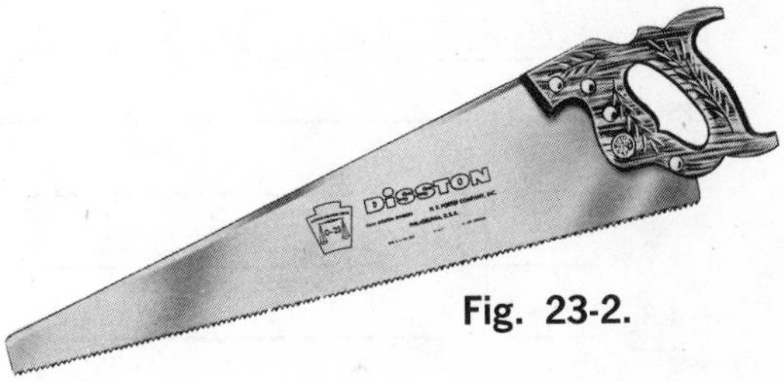

Fig. 23-2.

3. Fig. 23-3

   Name ______________________________

   Use ______________________________

   ____

   ____

   ____

   ____

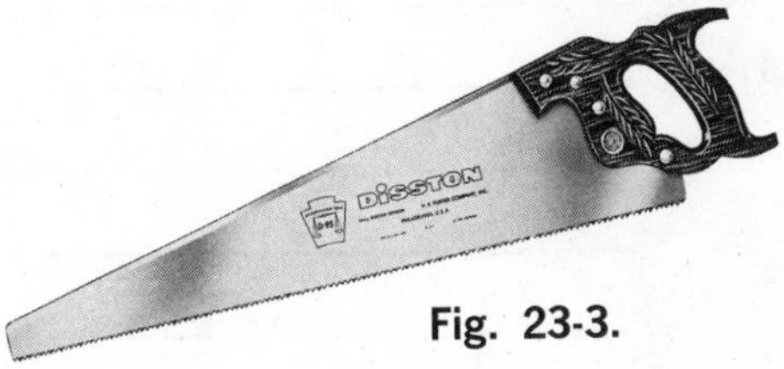

Fig. 23-3.

4. Fig. 23-4

   Name ______________________________

   Uses ______________________________

   ____

   ____

   ____

   ____

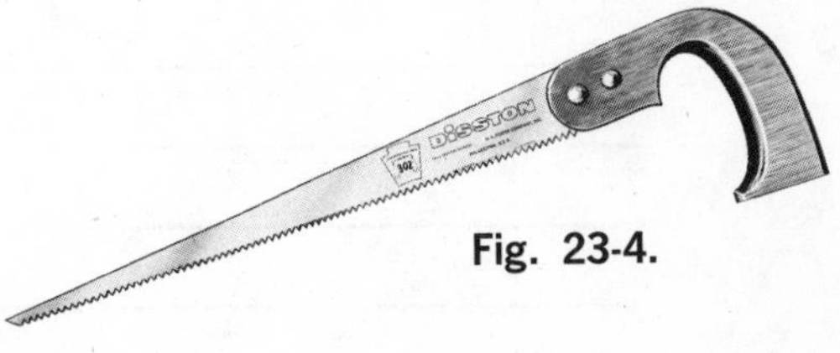

Fig. 23-4.

5. Fig. 23-5

   Name _____

   Use _____
        _____
        _____
        _____
        _____

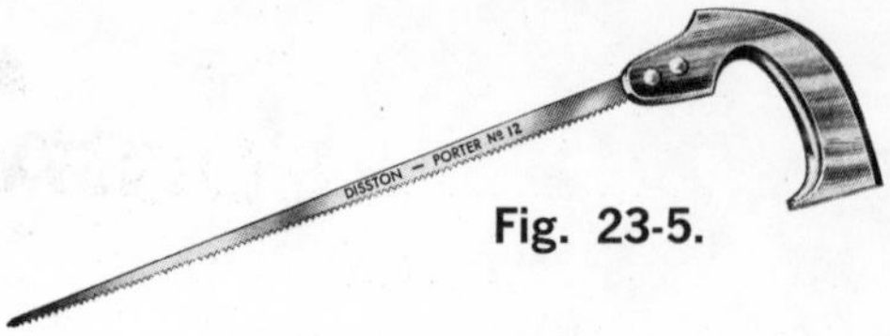

Fig. 23-5.

6. Fig. 23-6

   Name _____

   Uses _____
        _____
        _____
        _____
        _____

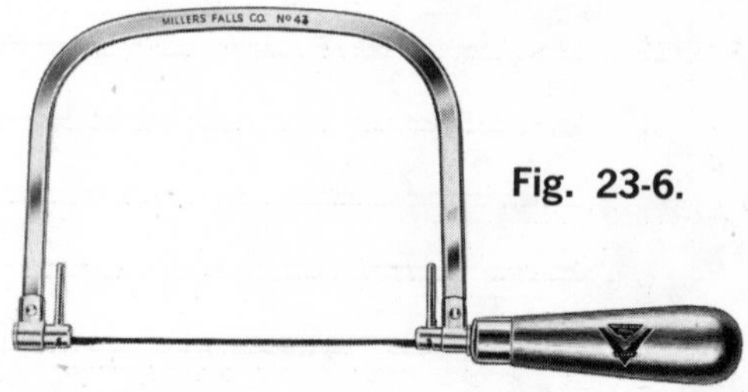

Fig. 23-6.

7. Fig. 23-7

   Name _____

   Use _____
        _____
        _____
        _____
        _____

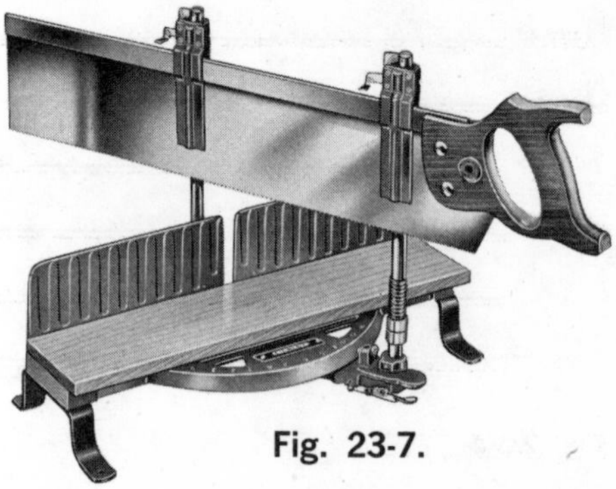

Fig. 23-7.

8. Fig. 23-8

   Name _____

   Use _____
        _____
        _____
        _____
        _____

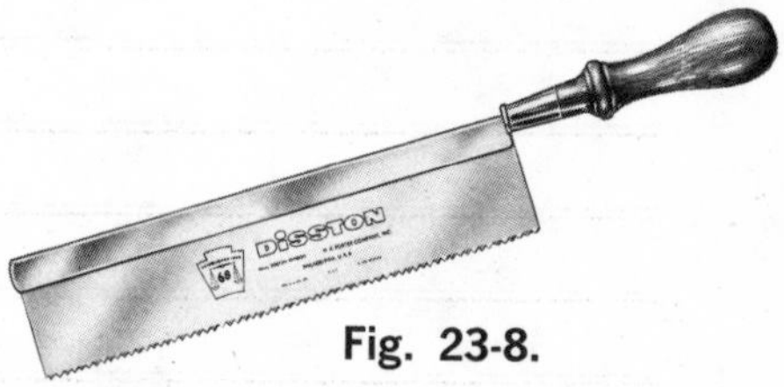

Fig. 23-8.

9. Fig. 23-9

   Name _____

   Use _____
        _____
        _____
        _____

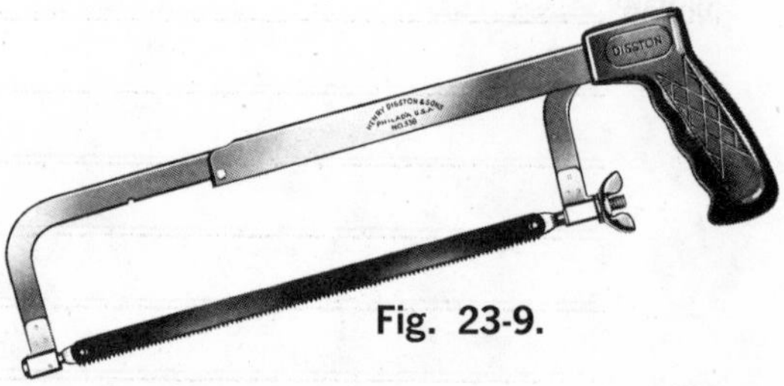

Fig. 23-9.

Section D—Unit 24 Name ____________________

Pages 304–306 Score __________

Study Guide No. 24

EDGE-CUTTING TOOLS

Checking Your Knowledge

1. Fig. 24-1

   Name ____________________

   Uses ____________________

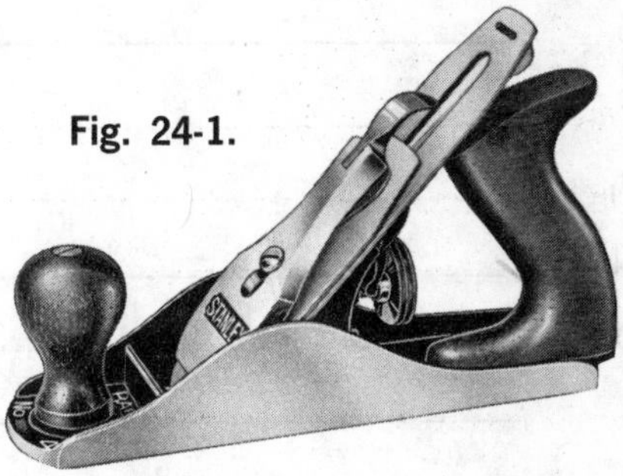

Fig. 24-1.

2. Fig. 24-2

   Name ____________________

   Uses ____________________

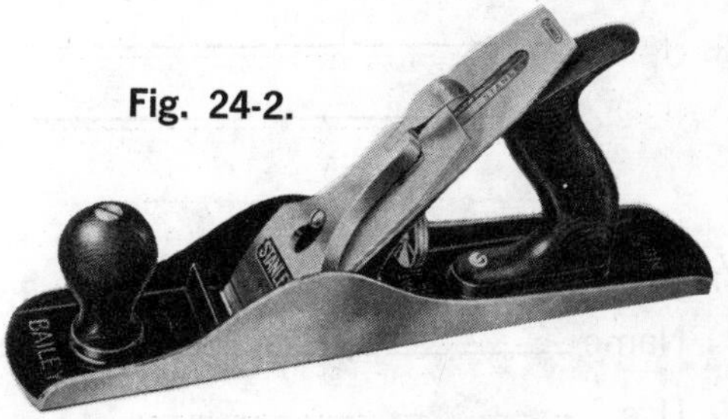

Fig. 24-2.

3. Fig. 24-3

   Name ____________________

   Use ____________________

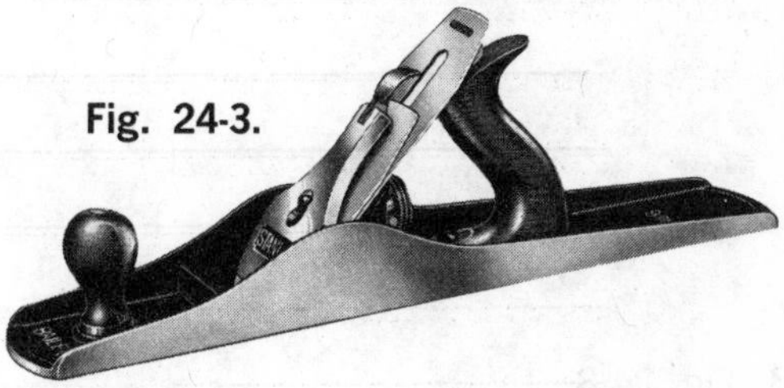

Fig. 24-3.

4. Fig. 24-4

   Name ____________________

   Uses ____________________

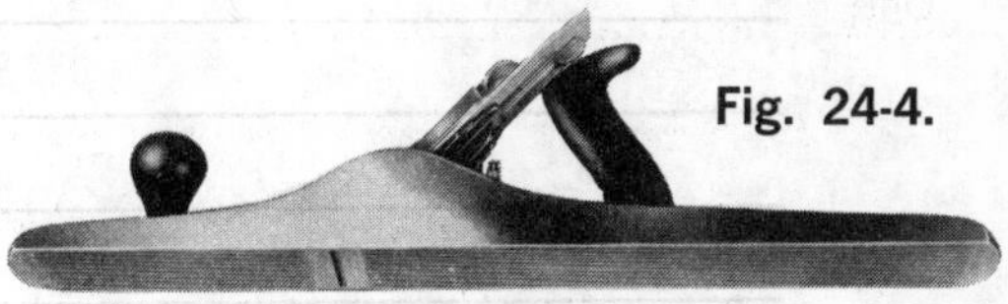

Fig. 24-4.

5. Fig. 24-5

    Name _____

    Use   _____

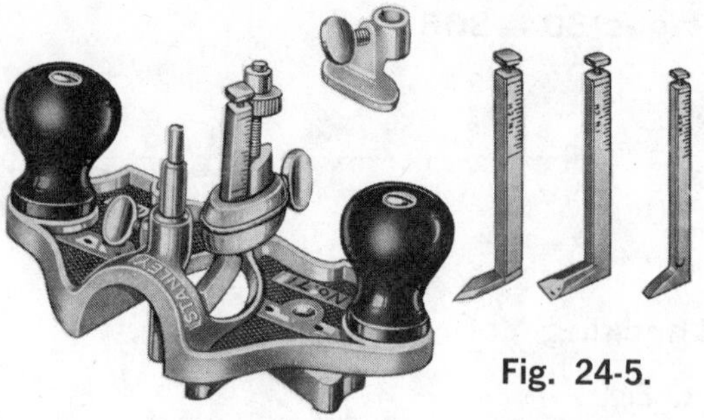

           _____

           _____

           _____

           _____

Fig. 24-5.

6. Fig. 24-6

    Name _____

    Uses _____

Fig. 24-6.

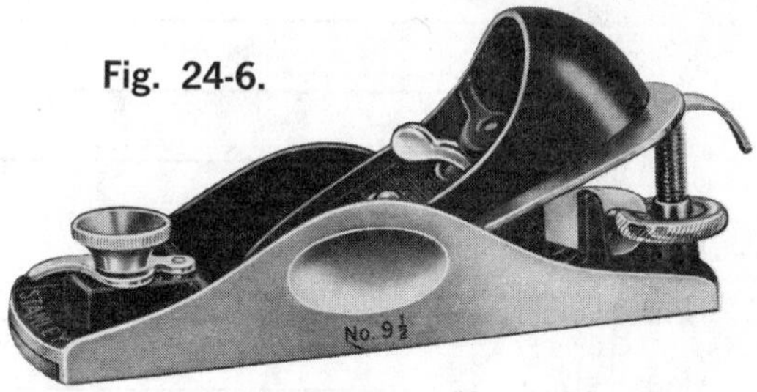

           _____

           _____

           _____

           _____

7. Fig. 24-7

    Name _____

    Use   _____

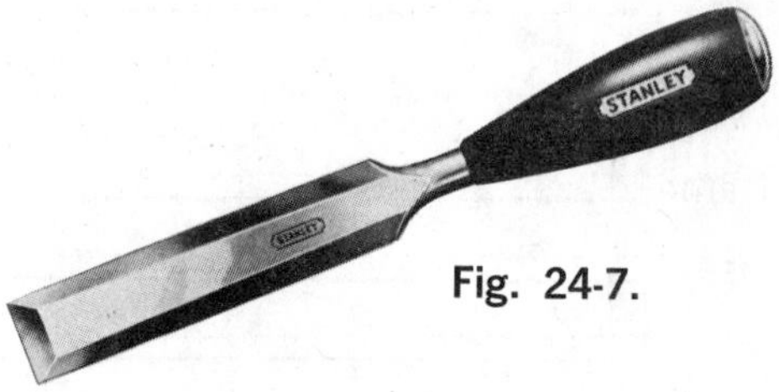

            _____

           _____

           _____

Fig. 24-7.

           _____

           _____

8. Fig. 24-8

    Name _____

    Use   _____

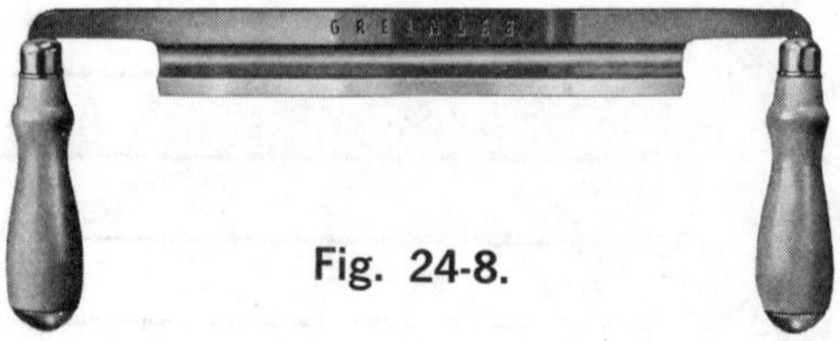

           _____

           _____

           _____

Fig. 24-8.

9. Fig. 24-9

   Name _____

   Use _____

   _____

   _____

   _____

   _____

   _____

Fig. 24-9.

10. Fig. 24-10

   Name _____

   Use _____

   _____

   _____

   _____

   _____

Fig. 24-10.

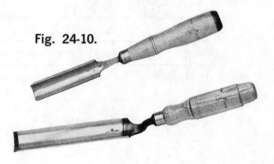

11. Fig. 24-11

   Name _____

   Use _____

   _____

   _____

   _____

   _____

Fig. 24-11.

12. Fig. 24-12

   Name _____

   Use _____

   _____

   _____

   _____

   _____

   _____

Fig. 24-12.

13. Fig. 24-13

Name _____

Use _____

_____

_____

_____

_____

Fig. 24-13.

14. Fig. 24-14

Name _____

Use _____

_____

_____

_____

Fig. 24-14.

Section D—Unit 25 Name ________________

Pages 307–308 Score ________

Study Guide No. 25

DRILLING AND BORING TOOLS

Checking Your Knowledge

1. Fig. 25-1

Name ________________

Uses ________________

____

____

____

____

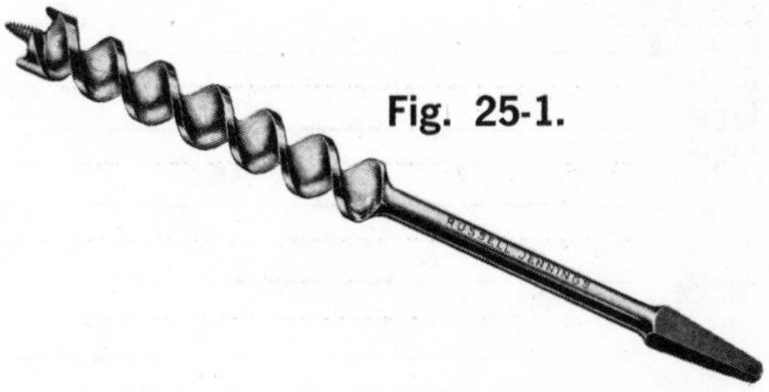

Fig. 25-1.

2. Fig. 25-2

Name ________________

Use ________________

____

____

____

____

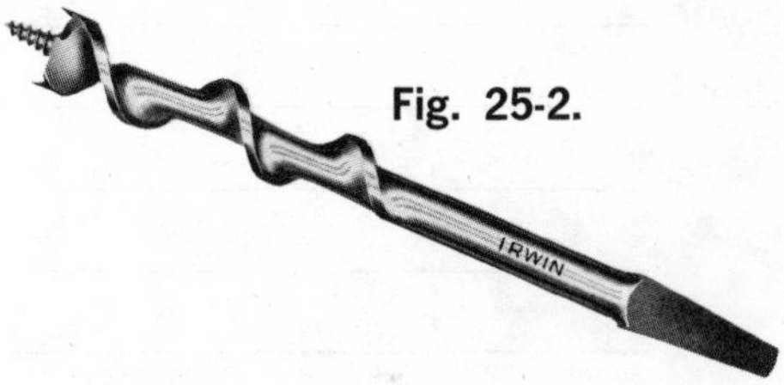

Fig. 25-2.

3. Fig. 25-3

Name ________________

Uses ________________

____

____

____

____

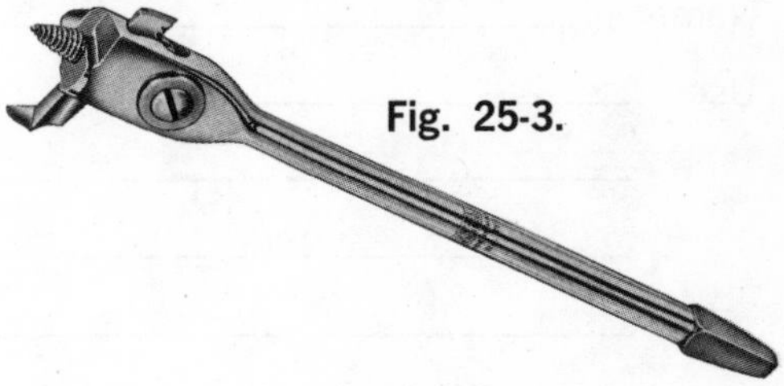

Fig. 25-3.

4. Fig. 25-4

Name ________________

Use ________________

____

____

____

____

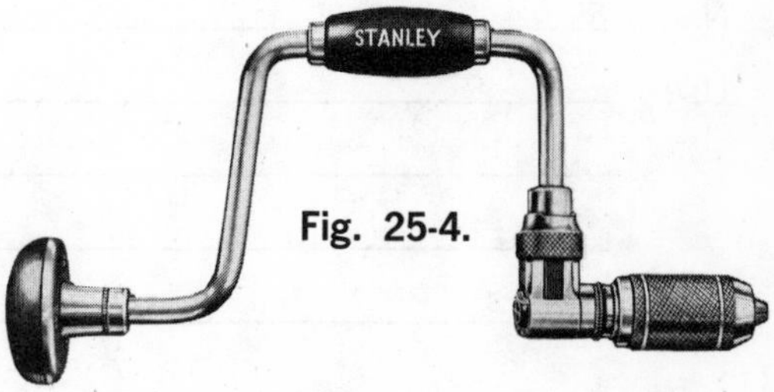

Fig. 25-4.

5. Fig. 25-5

   Name _____

   Uses _____

   _____

   _____

   _____

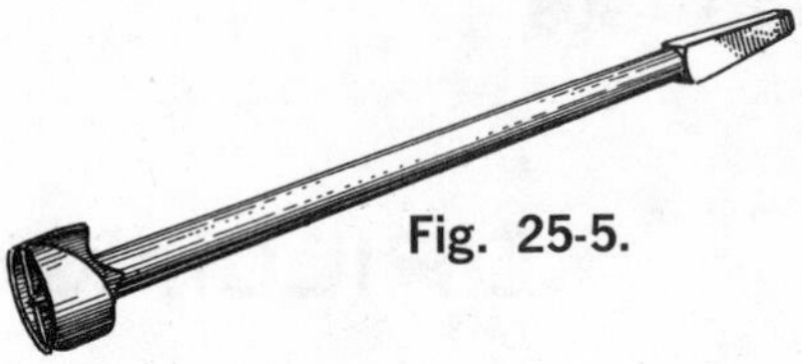

   Fig. 25-5.

6. Fig. 25-6

   Name _____

   Use _____

   _____

   _____

   _____

   _____

   Fig. 25-6.

7. Fig. 25-7

   Name _____

   Use _____

   _____

   _____

   _____

   _____

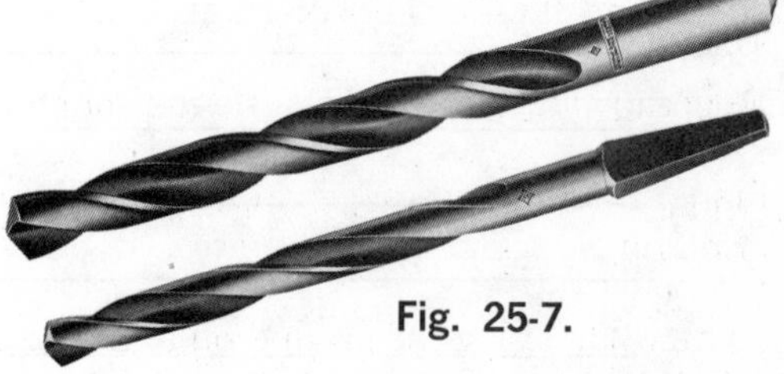

   Fig. 25-7.

8. Fig. 25-8

   Name _____

   Use _____

   _____

   _____

   _____

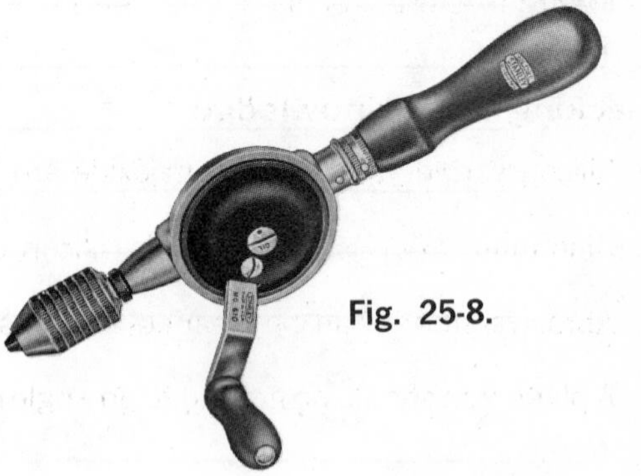

   Fig. 25-8.

9. Fig. 25-9

   Name _____

   Use _____

   _____

   _____

   _____

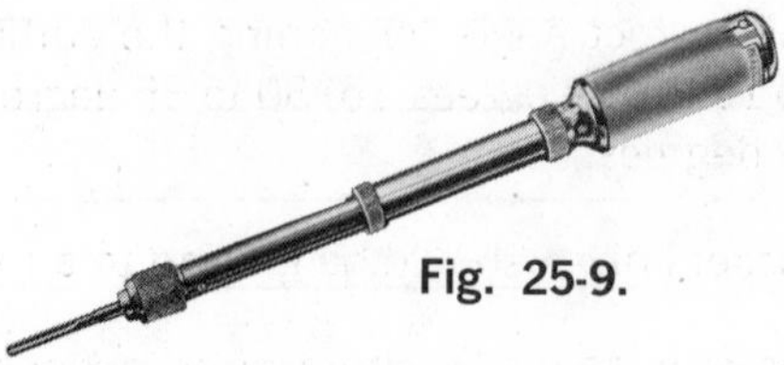

   Fig. 25-9.

Study Guide No. 26
TOOL SHARPENING

Reviewing the Main Ideas

1. The key to successful woodworking is _____ cutting tools.

_____

2. There are two classes of sharpening stones, natural and _____.

_____

3. Two types of artificial stones are those made of silicon carbide and _____ _____.

_____

4. Sharpening plane irons involves two steps: _____ to the correct angle and honing the edge.

_____

5. Tools that must be ground and _____ to a cutting edge include the plane iron, chisel, hatchet, pocket knife, and draw knife.

_____

6. The auger bit must be sharpened by filing the upper side of the cutting edges and the inside of the _____.

_____

7. Wood-turning tools are sharpened much like a _____.

_____

8. Planer or surfacer knives are usually sharpened on the machine with a grinding _____.

_____

9. Jointer knives can be ground on a _____ _____, a circular saw, or a grinder. (See text, Fig. 26-13.)

_____

10. Hand and machine-saw _____ should be sent to a commercial establishment for saw filing.

_____

Checking Your Knowledge

1. Silicon carbide and aluminum oxide are _____ abrasives.

_____

2. Aluminum oxide is tougher than silicon oxide. T or F

_____

3. Abrasive stones can be cleaned with gasoline or _____.

_____

4. A plane iron should be ground to an angle of _____ to _____ degrees.

_____

5. The correct angle for honing the cutting edge of a plane-iron blade is: (a) 10 to 20 degrees, (b) 30 to 35 degrees, (c) 20 to 25 degrees, (d) 20 to 35 degrees.

_____

6. Pocket knives should be ground to an angle of about 45 degrees. T or F

_____

7. The outside of the spurs of an auger bit should be filed. T or F

_____

8. Match the turning tools at the left to the correct angles for sharpening at the right:

a. round nose   1. 35° for hardwood

b. parting tool   2. round end and 30°

c. spear point   3. pointed end and 30°

d. skew   4. 45°

e. gouge   5. 40°

f. flat nose   6. 60°

a. _____

b. _____

c. _____

d. _____

e. _____

f. _____

9. The tip of a screwdriver should be sharpened to a round end. T or F

_____

10. The honing of jointer knives can be done with the knives on the machine. (See text, Fig. 26-14.) T or F

_____

11. Both sides of a pocket knife must be honed equally. T or F

_____

12. The first step in sharpening a chisel is to hone the edge. T or F

_____

13. Check the spelling of the following words. If correct, place a "C" in the space. If incorrect, give the correct spelling.

a. Abrasive

_____

b. Honeing

_____

c. Countersink

_____

d. Sharpening

_____

Name_____

Score_____

Study Guide No. 27
COMMON OPERATIONS AND PRINCIPLES

Reviewing the Main Ideas

1. Woodworking machinery is used in every step, from cutting and processing raw materials to the completion of the wood _____.

   _____

2. There are many common _____ that can be made with woodworking machinery including the groove, dado, rabbet, chamfer, bevel, taper, and mortise-and-tenon.

   _____

3. A knowledge of the following is needed when machining wood: characteristics of the wood and of the machine, correct setup, and the _____ of the machine.

   _____

4. In surfacing lumber, the number of knife marks per inch can be controlled by the rate of _____.

   _____

5. Common problems in planing are: raised grain, torn or chipped _____, fuzzy grain, machine burns, and chip marks.

   _____

6. An alloy of carbon and such metallic elements as tungsten, titanium, or tantalum is called _____.

   _____

7. Carbide-tipped tools give a smoother cut, last longer, and need _____ less than high-speed steel tools.

   _____

8. Common terms in power _____ include: machine, work, force, and friction.

   _____

9. The six simple basic machines are the inclined _____, wedge, screw, lever, wheel and axle, and pulley.

   _____

10. Belts and pulleys are used to transmit power and provide a method of changing the _____ of a machine tool.

    _____

11. The common pulley arrangements on wood machines are V belts and pulleys, and _____-speed pulleys with belt.

    _____

12. Other power _____ methods used on wood machines are direct drive, gear- or chain-driven feed mechanism, and reciprocating drive.

    _____

13. Correct maintenance of machines includes proper _____, keeping working parts and surfaces clean, sharpening knives and cutting tools, keeping safety devices in good condition, and taking care of belts, pulleys, and bearings.

    _____

Checking Your Knowledge

1. Identify these common cuts. Fig. 27-1:

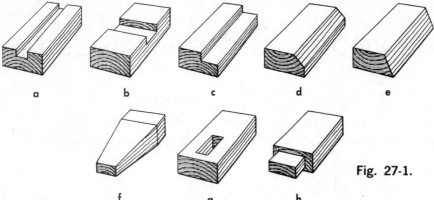

Fig. 27-1.

a. _____

b. _____

c. _____

d. _____

e. _____

f. _____

g. _____

h. _____

2. A knowledge of the characteristics of wood is one of the _____ (number) things that need to be known in machining wood.

_____

3. In machining woods, there are three principal objectives: (a) obtaining maximum surface _____, (b) maintaining maximum control over the _____, (c) getting the best results with the fewest _____ and lowest cost.

_____

_____

_____

4. Under a microscope, planed surface appears as a series of waves which are actually knife marks made when the lumber is fed across the revolving cutter head. T or F

_____

5. The waves formed by the knife marks of a planed surface are parallel to the direction of feed. T or F

_____

6. The quality of a planed surface is judged by the _____ of the knife marks per inch and by the _____ of the wave marks.

_____

7. Identify the terms shown in Fig. 27-2:

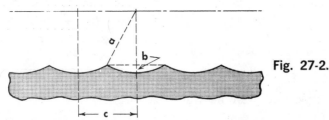

Fig. 27-2.

a. _____

b. _____

c. _____

8. A good planed surface should have about 10 or _____ knife marks per inch on dry lumber.

_____

9. Cross-grain and curly-grain work should have 20 or more knife marks per inch. T or F

_____

10. The motor is rated at 1725 RPM. The driver pulley is smaller than the driven pulley. The driven pulley will turn at: (a) 1725 RPM, (b) more than 1725 RPM, (c) less than 1725 RPM, (d) none of the answers is correct.

_____

11. If the speed of the motor, the diameter of the driver pulley, and the required speed of the machine are known, you can find the diameter of the driven pulley. T or F

_____

12. On variable-speed pulleys, the speed must be changed while the machine is running. T or F

_____

13. V belts and pulleys require that the speed be changed while the machine is stopped. T or F

_____

14. The direct drive is sometimes used on cut-off saws. T or F

_____

15. The two most common bearings used in most machines are _____ and _____ bearings.

_____

_____

16. V belts should be lubricated with oil and grease. T or F

_____

17. V belts run more quietly than flat belts. T or F

_____

18. Identify these common problems in planing a surface. Fig. 27-3:

a. _____

b. _____

c. _____

d. _____

a

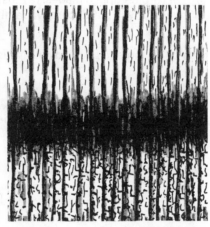

c

Fig. 27-3.

b

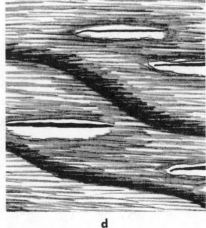

d

19. If the motor speed is 1725 RPM, the pulley on the motor is 1 1/2 inches in diameter, and the pulley on the saw is 4 inches in diameter, give the RPM of the saw.

_____

20. Suppose you want a shaper to operate at 6900 RPM with a motor that operates at 3450 RPM, and you have a 2-inch pulley on the motor. Tell what must be the diameter of the pulley on the shaper.

_____

21. The drill press is a good example of a machine that has rotating, reciprocating motion. T or F

_____

22. Match the six simple machines at the left to examples of their use at the right:

a. inclined plane	1. handle of drill press
b. wedge	2. clamp on lathe
c. screw	3. guard on jointer
d. lever	4. circular saw blade
e. wheel and axle	5. thread on mortiser
f. pulley	6. pulleys on jigsaw

a. _____

b. _____

c. _____

d. _____

e. _____

f. _____

23. One of the following is *not* an advantage of carbide-tipped blades: (a) cost little, (b) give smoother cut, (c) last longer, (d) will cut decorative laminates.

_____

24. A device used to make work easier or to apply force to good advantage is a _____.

_____

25. A push or pull that can do work is called a _____.

_____

26. Check the spelling of the following words. If correct, place a "C" in the space. If incorrect, give the correct spelling.

a. Principles

_____

b. Charecteristics

_____

c. Carbide

_____

d. Mechanisam

_____

Section D—Unit 28
Pages 328–338

Name ____________________

Score ________

Study Guide No. 28

RADIAL-ARM SAW

Reviewing the Main Ideas

1. An upside-down saw that can do many different types of cutting is called the ______ saw. ____________
2. The radial-arm saw is extremely popular with ______ and builders because of its great flexibility. ____________
3. For crosscutting, mitering, dadoing, and similar operations, the work is held firmly to the ______. ____________
4. The size of the radial-arm saw is determined by the ______ of the blade and the horsepower (kilowatt) rating. ____________
5. Crosscutting is done with the radial arm at ______ angles to the guide fence. ____________
6. Ripping is done with the blade ______ to the guide fence. ____________

Checking Your Knowledge

1. Name the parts of a radial-arm saw. Fig. 28-1:

a. ____________
b. ____________
c. ____________
d. ____________
e. ____________
f. ____________
g. ____________
h. ____________
i. ____________
j. ____________
k. ____________
l. ____________
m. ____________
n. ____________

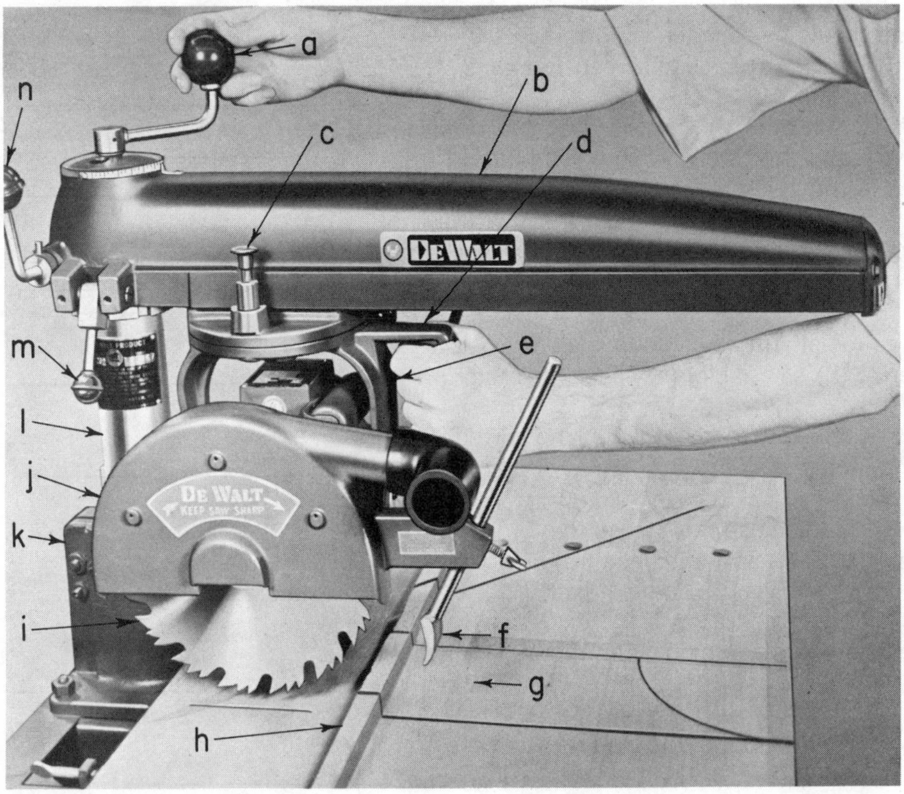

Fig. 28-1.

2. To raise or lower the blade on a radial-arm saw, the _____ handle must be turned.

_____

3. When crosscutting on a radial-arm saw, the anti-kickback device should clear the top of the work by about _____ (inches).

_____

4. When crosscutting on a radial-arm saw, always cut on the backward stroke. T or F

_____

5. When ripping on a radial-arm saw, the blade should rotate upward and toward you. T or F

_____

6. When crosscutting, the anti-kickback device should be: (a) raised to clear the surface of the stock, (b) set to drag on the face of the stock, (c) used the same as when ripping, (d) not used at all.

_____

7. When crosscutting with the radial-arm saw, the cut is made from the _____ stroke.

_____

8. The size of a radial-arm saw is determined by the diameter of the _____ and the _____ rating.

_____

_____

9. When using the radial-arm saw for ripping, the stock can be fed from either end. T or F

_____

10. Motor and blade can be tilted in an arc of: (a) 90°, (b) 180°, (c) 270°, (d) 360°.

_____

11. Before stock is cut, the saw blade should be adjusted so that it cuts the wood table by about: (a) 1/32″ (0.8 mm), (b) 1/16″ (1.6 mm), (c) 3/8″ (9.5 mm), (d) 1/4″ (6.4 mm).

_____

12. When the radial-arm saw is set up for ripping, the yoke should be turned until the blade is at right angles to the guide fence. T or F

_____

13. For ripping operations the cutting head is stationary and the workpiece is moved. T or F

_____

14. One of the following parts of the radial-arm saw cannot be moved to make adjustments: (a) radial arm, (b) saw table, (c) yoke, (d) motor.

_____

15. To make a simple miter cut, move the _____ _____ to the correct position.

_____

16. To make a hopper cut, the following two adjustments need to be made: (a) motor and yoke, (b) motor and arm, (c) arm and yoke, (d) arm and table.

_____

17. A dado wider than the dado head can be made by moving the material after each pass. T or F

_____

18. When ripping, the guard should be adjusted so that the infeed end clears the work by about _____ (millimetres).

_____

Study Guide No 28 (Continued)　　　　　Name_____

19. Check the spelling of the following words. If correct, place a "C" in the
space. If incorrect, give the correct spelling.

　　a. Radial　　　　　　　　　　　　　　　　_____

　　b. Dadoeing　　　　　　　　　　　　　　_____

　　c. Bevel　　　　　　　　　　　　　　　　_____

　　d. Hopper　　　　　　　　　　　　　　　_____

　　e. Compuond　　　　　　　　　　　　　　_____

Name_____

Score_____

Study Guide No. 29
PLANER OR SURFACER

Reviewing the Main Ideas

1. The size of the planer is indicated by the _____ of work it will handle.

   _____

2. The single surfacer is used to cut stock to _____ after warp has been removed.

   _____

3. The chip breaker holds the stock firmly on the bed and prevents the knives from _____ the wood surface.

   _____

4. The top or upper infeed roll has a _____ surface to grip the stock.

   _____

5. The chip breaker on a large machine is made in _____ so that wood of slightly different thicknesses can be fed into the machine at the same time.

   _____

6. A common use for the planer is to square up _____ for furniture legs.

   _____

Checking Your Knowledge

1. Another name for the planer is the _____.

   _____

2. A planer that surfaces both sides at the same time is called a _____ surfacer.

   _____

3. The cutter head of a surfacer is similar to that of a _____.

   _____

4. Depth of cut should be set: (a) while the machine is running and no stock is being fed into it, (b) at any time, (c) while the stock is being machined, (d) when the machine is at a dead stop.

   _____

5. Whether stock is varnished or painted makes no difference as far as planing is concerned. T or F

   _____

6. The primary use of a planer is to surface the edges of boards. T or F

   _____

7. You should stand directly behind the stock as it is being fed into the planer. T or F

   _____

8. Never feed stock that is shorter than the distance between the _____ and _____ rolls.

   _____

   _____

9. The size of a planer is indicated by: (a) the thickness of the stock surfaced, (b) the width of the stock surfaced, (c) the capacity (thickness and width) of the stock handled, (d) the height of the machine.

   _____

10. The joined side of a board should be down when you feed it into a planer. T or F

   _____

11. If the distance between the infeed and outfeed roll is 16″ (406.4 mm), then the shortest board that can be surfaced is: (a) 12″ (304.8 mm), (b) 16″ (406.4 mm), (c) 18″ (457.2 mm), (d) 20″ (508 mm).

12. Adjust the planer so that it will take a rough cut of about: (a) 1/4″ (6.4 mm), (b) 1/2″ (12.7 mm), (c) 1/16″ (1.6 mm), (d) 3/8″ (9.5 mm).

13. If stock measures 25/32 inch in thickness, then the planer should be set at: (a) 3/4″, (b) 7/8″, (c) 23/32″, (d) 1″.

14. Name the parts in the cutting roller assembly. Fig. 29-1:

a. _____

b. _____

c. _____

d. _____

e. _____

Fig. 29-1.

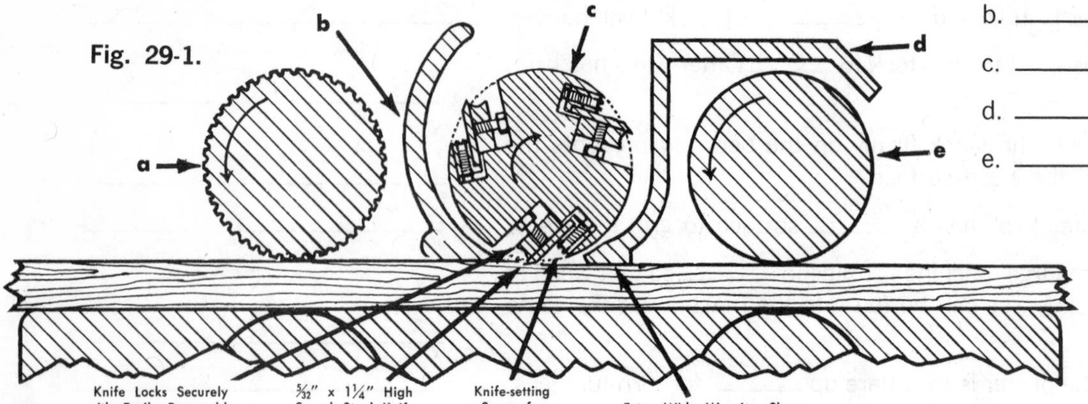

Knife Locks Securely with Easily Removable Safety-type Shim   5/32″ x 1¼″ High Speed Steel Knife for all Woods   Knife-setting Screw for Quick Adjustment   Extra Wide Wearing Shoe

15. The purpose of the chip breaker is to: (a) apply pressure to the stock after it has passed the knife, (b) increase pressure on the outfeed rolls, (c) prevent the knives from tearing the grain, (d) remove irregular surfaces from the stock.

16. The main infeed roll of the planer should be: (a) smooth, (b) corrugated, (c) wavy, (d) irregular.

17. When removing a large amount of material on the planer, all cuts should be made from one side of the stock. T or F

18. The final cut should allow from _____ to _____ (inches) for hand work including sanding.

19. After the stock is gripped by the infeed rolls, the operator should: (a) keep pushing the stock, (b) increase the feed, (c) keep hands away from the material, (d) adjust the depth of cut.

20. Check the spelling of the following words. If correct, place a "C" in the space. If incorrect, give the correct spelling.

    a. Surfacer

    b. Corrugated

    c. Pressuer bar

Study Guide No. 30
CIRCULAR SAW

Reviewing the Main Ideas

1. The circular saw is a very versatile machine which can be used in _____ (making joints).

2. The size of the circular saw is given in inches (or millimetres) which represent the diameter of the _____.

3. The _____ saw can be used for ripping, crosscutting, mitering, and many other operations.

4. The splitter, _____, and anti-kickback are used to reduce accidental injury to the operator.

5. All types of miter and bevel _____ can be made with the circular saw.

6. The circular saw can be used for cutting dadoes by attaching a _____ _____.

7. The circular saw can also be used to cut _____ for mortise-and-tenon joints.

8. Tapers can be cut on the circular saw, using one of the three types of simple _____.

_____

_____

_____

_____

_____

_____

_____

_____

Checking Your Knowledge

1. Name the parts of the circular saw. Fig. 30-1:

Fig. 30-1.

a. _____
b. _____
c. _____
d. _____
e. _____
f. _____
g. _____
h. _____
i. _____
j. _____

2. A circular saw with one arbor is called a _____ saw.

3. An accessory that cuts all widths of grooves from 1/8 inch (3 mm) to 13/16 inch (21 mm) is called a: (a) dado head, (b) molding head, (c) cutter head, (d) grooving head.

4. The saw blade should protrude above the stock about: (a) 1/4″ (6 mm) or more, (b) 1/8″ (3 mm), (c) 1/2″ (13 mm), (d) 1″ (25 mm).

5. When cutting small pieces on the circular saw, hold the wood in a "freehand" manner. T or F

6. The attachment used as a guide for all ripping operations is called a _____.

7. A combination blade can be used for both ripping and crosscutting. T or F

8. Always stand directly in back of the saw blade. T or F

9. Use a push stick when ripping narrow strips to width. T or F

10. When crosscutting, the material is held against: (a) a fence, (b) a miter gauge, (c) an angle gauge, (d) a tilt gauge.

11. If the ripping fence is used to cut identical pieces to length, always clamp a _____ _____ to it.

12. The metal device that is attached to the miter gauge for cutting identical pieces to length is called a _____ _____.

13. The compound miter joint is sometimes called a _____ joint.

14. To make a compound miter cut with the tilt of work at 45 degrees (on a 4-side butt), the blade should be tilted _____ degrees and the miter gauge should be set at _____ degrees.

15. When feeding narrow stock between the blade and the fence, always use a _____ _____.

16. When cutting plywood on the circular saw, always place the stock with the _____ side up.

17. Cutting thick stock into thinner boards is called _____.

18. The standard dado head consists of inside _____ and _____ cutters.

19. The outside cutters are 1/8 inch (3 mm) in thickness. T or F

20. The dado head can be used for cutting a tenon. T or F

21. A commercial jig is available for cutting tenons. T or F

22. The two cuts necessary to make a tenon are the _____ cut and the _____ cut.

23. The splitter is on a circular saw to: (a) give added strength to the saw, (b) prevent the wood from pinching the saw and kicking back, (c) keep the saw clean, (d) make a guide unnecessary.

24. The device shown in Fig. 30-2 is called a _____ _____.

25. When dadoing across the end of work, it is best to speed up the feed at the end of the cut. T or F

26. When using a circular saw to rip stock, you should stand: (a) at the left side of the saw, (b) directly in front of the saw, (c) directly back of the saw, (d) it doesn't matter where you stand.

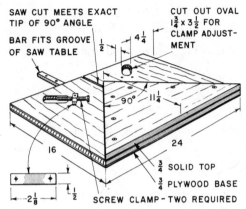

SAW CUT MEETS EXACT TIP OF 90° ANGLE
BAR FITS GROOVE OF SAW TABLE
CUT OUT OVAL 1¾ x 3½ FOR CLAMP ADJUST-MENT
4¼
½
90°
11¼
16
24
2⅛
½
¾ SOLID TOP
¾ PLYWOOD BASE
SCREW CLAMP—TWO REQUIRED
⅛ IRON STRAP HOLDS CLAMP IN PLACE

Fig. 30-2.

27. For making the miter cut shown in the text in Fig. 30-17, the blade is _____ and the work is held against the miter gauge.

28. The device shown in the text in Fig. 30-21 is called a _____ _____.

29. To cut a 5/16″ (8 mm) dado with one pass requires: (a) two cutters and one 1/8″ (3 mm) chipper, (b) two cutters and two chippers, (c) two cutters and a 1/16″ (2 mm), (d) two cutters and two 1/8″ (3 mm) chippers.

30. Make all adjustments on the saw: (a) when the machine is at a dead stop, (b) while the power is on, (c) during the cutting operation, (d) just after the switch is turned off.

31. Check the spelling of the following words. If correct, place a "C" in the space. If incorrect, give the correct spelling.

    a. Variety

    b. Univearsal

    c. Combination

    d. Grooveing

    e. Tenoning

    f. Taper

Name_____

Score_____

Study Guide No. 31
BAND SAW

Reviewing the Main Ideas

1. The band saw is used primarily to cut edges that are not _____.

2. The size of the band saw is determined by the _____ of the wheel.

3. The blade of the band saw is a thin flexible strip of steel, generally from 1/4 inch (6 mm) to 1/2 inch (13 mm) wide, with _____ along one edge.

4. The bottom wheel where the shaft of the motor is attached to the frame and cannot be adjusted is called the lower or _____ wheel.

5. The top wheel can be tilted so that the blade will run straight and also can be heightened to apply _____ to the blade.

6. Because the saw _____ is flexible, it is necessary to have a blade support and guides to keep it running true and to prevent it from twisting.

7. The _____ saw is used for cutting curves. It is not a precision machine.

8. The band saw can also be used for cutting straight lines by using a _____ or pivot block.

9. The band saw can be used to _____ stock to smaller thickness. In industry a separate machine much like a band saw, but with power feed, is used for resawing.

Checking Your Knowledge

1. The primary purpose of a band saw is for cutting curved edges. T or F

2. Very large band saws are called _____ _____.

3. The sharper the curve to be cut, the wider the blade should be. T or F

4. Always make long cuts first and then shorter cuts. T or F

5. The size of the band saw is equal to: (a) the largest thickness of stock that can be cut, (b) diameter of the wheels, (c) blade length, (d) the width of stock that can be cut.

6. The blade is made to track on the center of the wheel by: (a) adjusting the guide blocks, (b) tilting the table, (c) tilting the bottom wheel, (d) tilting the top wheel.

7. If the saw blade is not in near-perfect condition, then the following attachment should be used for resawing: (a) fence, (b) pivot block, (c) cutting jig, (d) miter gauge.

8. When resawing, always use the narrowest blade available. T or F

9. For cutting a 1/2-inch (13 mm) diameter circle, use a _____ (inches) width blade. (See text, Fig. 31-13b.)

10. Name the parts of the band saw. Fig. 31-1:

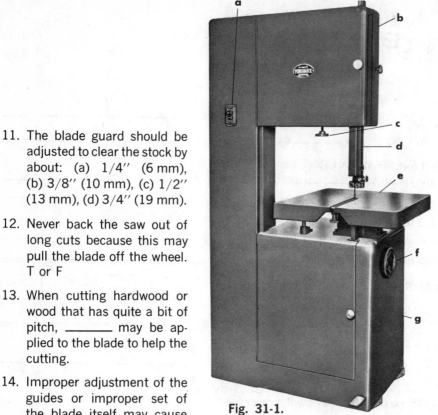

Fig. 31-1.

11. The blade guard should be adjusted to clear the stock by about: (a) 1/4″ (6 mm), (b) 3/8″ (10 mm), (c) 1/2″ (13 mm), (d) 3/4″ (19 mm).

12. Never back the saw out of long cuts because this may pull the blade off the wheel. T or F

13. When cutting hardwood or wood that has quite a bit of pitch, _____ may be applied to the blade to help the cutting.

14. Improper adjustment of the guides or improper set of the blade itself may cause _____.

15. Check the spelling of the following words. If correct, place a "C" in the space. If incorrect, give the correct spelling.

   a. Tension

   b. Coileing

   c. Resawing

   d. Turning

a. _____
b. _____
c. _____
d. _____
e. _____
f. _____
g. _____

_____

_____

_____

_____

_____

_____

_____

_____

110

Study Guide No. 32
JIG OR SCROLL SAW

Reviewing the Main Ideas

1. The jig or scroll saw is used primarily to cut inside and outside _____ parts of thin wood.

2. The jig or _____ saw has limited industrial use except for the pattern maker, but it is used by the sign maker and the model maker for cutting intricate designs.

3. Generally, a blade with the _____ teeth that will cut cleanly and follow the layout line is chosen.

4. Thin metal can be _____ between two pieces of wood for cutting.

5. On a jigsaw, the lower chuck does the _____ of the blade.

6. If a saber blade is used for internal cutting, it is held only in the _____ jaw.

Checking Your Knowledge

1. Another name for the jigsaw is the _____ saw.

2. The jigsaw can be used for cutting internal openings. T or F

3. The size of a jigsaw is shown by: (a) the size of the blade, (b) the size of the table, (c) the distance from the blade to the overarm, (d) the length of the blade.

4. When selecting a blade for the jigsaw, make sure that _____ teeth are in contact with the stock at all times.

5. The jigsaw is a very safe machine to use. T or F

6. The table of a jigsaw tilts. T or F

7. According to Fig. 32-3 in the text, a blade for cutting wood panel and veneer should have _____ teeth per inch.

8. Both wood and metal can be cut on a jigsaw. T or F

9. Carpenters prefer a stationary type jigsaw. T or F

10. The highest speed should be used when cutting metal. T or F

11. The two medium speeds should be used when cutting _____.

12. A jigsaw should cut on the down stroke of the blade. T or F

13. The correct blade for sawing hard and soft woods should have from _____ to _____ teeth per inch.

14. A saw blade for cutting a piece of hardware made from brass should have ——————— (number) teeth per inch.

15. Check the spelling of the following words. If correct, place a "C" in the space. If incorrect, give the correct spelling.

   a. Scrol

   b. Celluloid

   c. Pattern

   d. Externail

Study Guide No. 33
PORTABLE SAWS—CHAIN AND CUT-OFF

Reviewing the Main Ideas

1. A portable saw used for felling and bucking logs is called a _____ saw.

2. In using a gasoline chain saw, stand _____ the engine end of the saw.

3. When carrying the chain saw, grasp the top handle with bar and chain pointing to the _____.

4. Never use an electric chain saw in a damp or _____ location.

5. Before starting to saw, place your feet far enough apart to permit a comfortable but firm and _____ stance.

6. When the round tip of the saw is inserted into the wood rather than sawing with the underside or top of the guide bar, this is called making a _____ cut.

7. The fuel used for operating a gasoline chain saw must be a proper fuel/_____ mixture.

8. In sawing a tree, it is important to decide where to make the directional cut, or _____.

9. In sawing a tree, never saw all the way through the tree but leave a break-off allowance to act as a _____.

10. In removing limbs, kickback occurs when the guide bar _____ accidentally touches the branch.

11. The electric cut-off saw is designed primarily for on-the-job _____.

12. Other names for the electric cut-off saw are the power saw, hand saw, or _____ saw.

13. The saw is rated primarily by the _____ size, although the size of the motor is also important.

14. This saw is commonly used by _____ for rough cutting of framing material and for cutting stock after it has been nailed together.

Checking Your Knowledge

1. The term "bucking" is used when logs are cut in sections. T or F

2. The electric model chain saw is the most commonly used. T or F

3. One of the following is not a piece of safety equipment used when cutting with a chain saw: (a) safety glasses, (b) gloves, (c) loose-fitting clothing, (d) safety helmet.

4. Most electric chain saws come equipped with a three-prong safety plug. T or F

5. When sawing with the top side of the guide, the process is called "pulling chain". T or F

6. When the chain saw is idling, the chain should keep running. T or F

7. One of the following is not a factor which will affect the way in which the tree will fall: (a) the way it is leaning, (b) the size of the tree, (c) the wind velocity, (d) the slope of the earth.

8. When making a second cut in felling a tree, always cut completely through the tree. T or F

9. The risk of kickback is lowest when removing limbs from a fallen tree. T or F

10. When a log to be cut is supported on both ends with room underneath, always begin the cut from above. T or F

11. When it is necessary to work in a tree, always haul the saw along with you as you climb the tree. T and F

12. Identify the parts of the electric cut-off saw. Fig. 33-1:

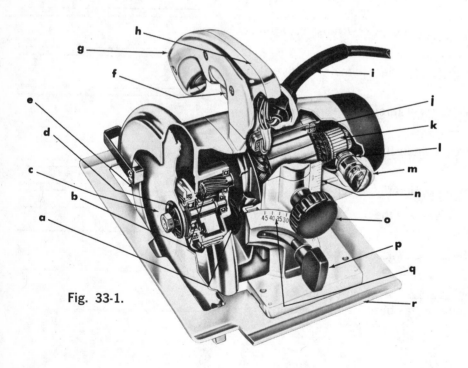

Fig. 33-1.

a. _____

b. _____

c. _____

d. _____

e. _____

f. _____

g. _____

h. _____

i. _____

j. _____

k. _____

l. _____

m. _____

n. _____

o. _____

p. _____

q. _____

r. _____

13. The most popular size of a cut-off saw is the _____ (millimetres) size.

14. Before using a portable electric cut-off saw, make sure it is grounded. T or F

114

15. If an extension cord for the saw must be 100′ (30 m) to 150′ (45 m) long, No. _____-gauge wire should be used.

_____

16. When using the saw for cutting plywood, always cut with the best face _____.

_____

17. Electric cut-off saws range from _____ to _____ (inches) in blade size.

_____

_____

18. The saw blade should be adjusted to protrude about _____ (millimetres) below the work.

_____

19. The saw can be used to trim uneven boards after they have been nailed in place. T or F

_____

20. The depth of cut is the same when the saw is set at a bevel angle as when it is set for a straight cut. T or F

_____

21. An opening cut in the middle of a wide piece of work is called a _____ cut.

_____

22. When ripping stock with the saw, it is a good idea to use: (a) a freehand method, (b) the ripping guide, (c) the fence, (d) a miter gauge.

_____

23. The following person would have the most use for a cut-off saw: (a) cabinetmaker, (b) patternmaker, (c) carpenter, (d) machinist.

_____

24. If the saw slows down or stalls, turn off the switch and then release the saw. T or F

_____

25. Check the spelling of the following words. If correct, place a "C" in the space. If incorrect, give the correct spelling.

a. Telescoping

_____

b. Adjusteing

_____

c. Shaething

_____

d. Switch

_____

Name_____

Score_____

Study Guide No. 34
HAND JIG, SABER, OR BAYONET SAW

Reviewing the Main Ideas

1. The hand jigsaw is used primarily for straight and _____ cuts on the job.

2. Other names for the hand jigsaw are the _____ or bayonet saw.

3. Straight cutting can be done freehand or with use of a _____ fence or guide.

4. Curved or _____ cuts can be made freehand.

5. Circles can be cut using the ripping _____ as a radius arm.

Checking Your Knowledge

1. One of the following is *not* a common name for the saw shown in Fig. 34-1 in the text: (a) jig, (b) saber, (c) swing, (d) bayonet.

2. All types of hand jigsaws have a base that tilts for making bevel cuts. T or F

3. Making an inside cut without first drilling a hole is called _____ cutting.

4. The hand jigsaw changes rotary action to up-and-down action. T or F

5. Check the spelling of the following words. If correct, place a "C" in the space. If incorrect, give the correct spelling.

   a. Bayonet

   b. Riping giude

   c. Irragular

   d. Straight

Name_____

Score_____

Study Guide No. 35
JOINTER

Reviewing the Main Ideas

1. The jointer is used to _____ the surface, edge, or end of stock.

2. A jointer can also be used to _____ up stock.

3. The depth of cut is determined by the adjustment of the _____ table.

4. Both the front and rear _____ can be moved on the base or frame by turning the hand wheels.

5. The rear table is adjusted so that the top surface is tangent to the cutting circle of the _____ in the cutting head.

6. Face jointing stock on a jointer can be dangerous. Use a _____ block when face jointing short pieces.

7. The jointer can be used to do beveling and chamfering and to cut shallow, short, and long _____.

8. When cutting a deep rabbet on a jointer, it may be necessary to cut it in _____ passes.

9. A machine that does many operations not easily done on a jointer is called a _____ jointer-surfacer.

_____

_____

_____

_____

_____

_____

_____

_____

_____

Checking Your Knowledge

1. Identify the parts of the jointer. Fig. 35-1:

a. _____

b. _____

c. _____

d. _____

e. _____

f. _____

Fig. 35-1.

2. The size of a jointer is indicated by the _____ of the knives.

_____

3. The rear table should be adjusted for each different type of cut. T or F _____

4. If the rear table is too high, it will cut a "snipe" at the end. T or F _____

5. One of the following is *not* a common operation that can be performed on the jointer: (a) surfacing a board, (b) planing an edge, (c) making a shoulder cut on a tenon, (d) cutting a bevel. _____

6. The shortest length of stock that should be surfaced is: (a) no limit, (b) 6″ (150 mm), (c) 12″ (300 mm), (d) 18″ (460 mm). _____

7. For a very smooth cut on a jointer, take a cut of _____ (inches) or less. _____

8. Always keep the fence in the same position when planing the edges of many pieces of stock. T or F _____

9. The angle of a jointer fence can be checked with a sliding T bevel. T or F _____

10. When cutting a long taper on the jointer, divide the stock into an equal number of parts. T or F _____

11. When planing end grain, make a short cut at one end and then reverse the stock and feed from the opposite direction. T or F _____

12. The taper can be cut on a jointer by: (a) setting the fence at an angle, (b) raising the rear table, (c) lowering the front table, (d) placing the back end of the stock past the knives before starting the cut. _____

13. To cut a bevel on a jointer, the following must be done: (a) lower the rear table, (b) raise the rear table, (c) adjust the fence to the correct angle, (d) remove the guard. _____

14. The jointer will do the following: (a) cut one side of the board parallel to the other, (b) sand the board smooth, (c) leave grooves on the cut surface, (d) plane one surface smooth and true. _____

15. The fence of the jointer will: (a) not tilt, (b) tilt right or left, (c) tilt right only, (d) tilt left only. _____

16. In cutting a taper on the jointer, the starting point of the taper is placed over the lip of the: (a) rear table, (b) front table, (c) fence, (d) bed. _____

17. A chamfer can be cut on the jointer by: (a) lowering the front table, (b) moving the fence to the right or left, (c) raising the rear table, (d) tilting the fence. _____

18. The depth of cut on a jointer is determined by the setting of the: (a) rear table, (b) front table, (c) fence, (d) guard. _____

19. Another name for the rear table is the _____ table. _____

20. If the rear table is too high, it will cut a _____. _____

21. One of the following is *not* a reason the knives of the jointer need sharpening: (a) planed wood has a fuzzy look, (b) it's difficult to feed the stock, (c) stock moves easily over the knives, (d) stock chatters when cutting. _____

22. The safety device shown in Fig. 35-2 is called a _____ _____.

23. A good way to cut a rabbet with the grain is on a jointer. T or F

24. A Uniplane can surface stock up to _____ (millimetres) in width.

25. Check the spelling of the following words. If correct, place a "C" in the space. If incorrect, give the correct spelling.

    a. Infeed

    b. Knives

    c. Jointer

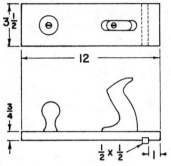

Fig. 35-2.

_____

_____

_____

_____

_____

_____

Name_____

Score_____

Study Guide No. 36
HAND OR POWER PLANE

Reviewing the Main Ideas

1. The portable _____ _____ is a labor-saving tool used for the same purposes as a hand plane except that it is much faster.

_____

2. The electric plane is especially useful to the _____.

_____

3. The power block plane is ideal for _____ work.

_____

Checking Your Knowledge

1. The electric hand plane is rated by its horsepower size. T or F

_____

2. The depth of cut on an electric hand plane can be varied. T or F

_____

3. A power block plane can be held in one hand. T or F

_____

4. A power block plane can plane 2-inch (100 mm) dressed lumber with a maximum cut of _____ (inches).

_____

5. With the carbide cutter, a power block plane can cut aluminum. T or F

_____

6. The electric hand plane can make bevel cuts. T or F

_____

7. The power block plane *cannot* be used for the following operation: (a) trimming edges of doors, (b) fitting drawers, (c) cutting a dado, (d) cutting a rabbet.

_____

8. Check the spelling of the following words. If correct, place a "C" in the space. If incorrect, give the correct spelling.

   a. Disconnect

_____

   b. Spirul

_____

   c. Adjustement

_____

Study Guide No. 37
ROUTER

Reviewing the Main Ideas

1. A router is a very versatile machine that can do a wide variety of _____, shaping, and routing jobs.

   _____

2. Some of the common cuts that can be made by the _____ are the rabbet, dado, mortise, and the dovetail, plus many types of edge cuts.

   _____

3. A portable router consists of a motor and a base with a collet chuck to hold the _____ tools.

   _____

4. A large _____ router is used in the furniture industry.

   _____

5. A portable router can be guided in the following ways: by a homemade guide block or T square, by using a straight or circular guide, by using a cutter with a pilot end, by using a template, and by _____ routing.

   _____

6. A portable router can also be used with a dovetail attachment to cut a _____ joint.

   _____

Checking Your Knowledge

1. Name these router bits. Fig. 37-1:

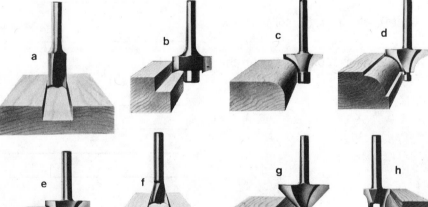

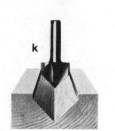

Fig. 37-1.

a. _____
b. _____
c. _____
d. _____
e. _____
f. _____
g. _____
h. _____
i. _____
j. _____
k. _____
l. _____

2. There are _____ main ways of controlling the sidewise movement of the router.

3. Fig. 37-2 shows a cutter with a _____ to control the depth of cut.

Fig. 37-2.

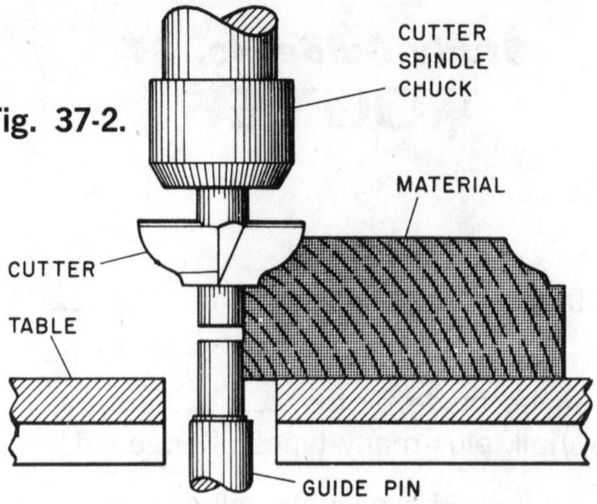

CUTTER
SPINDLE
CHUCK

MATERIAL

CUTTER

TABLE

GUIDE PIN

4. The router can be used in a freehand manner. T or F

5. Many decorative edges can be made with a portable router. T or F

6. The best drawer joint, the dovetail joint, is made with a router and a _____ attachment.

7. One of the carpentry jobs that can be done very rapidly with the router is cutting _____ for installing hinges.

8. Depth of cut in routing is controlled by the position of: (a) bit, (b) base, (c) guide, (d) shank.

9. The router cutter used to cut a groove is called a straight bit. T or F

10. The operator's skill determines the quality of _____ routing work.

11. When making a deep cut, do not attempt to cut to full depth with one cut. T or F

12. The cutting action of a router is: (a) reciprocating, (b) scraping, (c) rotary, (d) slicing.

13. Router bits are held in the spindle by: (a) set screw, (b) collet chuck, (c) tapered shank, (d) tapered pin.

14. Check the spelling of the following words. If correct, place a "C" in the space. If incorrect, give the correct spelling.

    a. Router

    b. Collete

    c. Rabbet

    d. Dovetaile

Study Guide No. 38
SHAPER

Reviewing the Main Ideas

1. The shaper can make cuts on the edges and _____ of stock whether it is straight or of irregular shape.

2. The safest shaper cutter is the _____ solid type.

3. The table of a shaper is usually fixed, but the _____ can usually be moved up and down.

4. There are many types of shaper _____ available, made of either high-speed or carbide tips.

5. The shaper runs at very high _____ of 7200 to 8500 RPM.

6. The three principal ways of controlling the depth of cut are with a fence, with a _____ collar, and with a pattern or form.

7. Always feed the stock _____ the rotation of the cutter.

8. The hand-feed shaper is the most _____ of the common woodworking machines; exact safety rules must be followed before and during its operation.

Checking Your Knowledge

1. The shaper is a very safe machine to use. T or F

2. The shaper operates at speeds from _____ to _____ RPM.

3. Always feed stock into a cutter in the same direction as the cutter rotation. T or F

4. The shortest piece that should be shaped is: (a) 10″ (250 mm), (b) 12″ (300 mm), (c) 16″ (405 mm), (d) 20″ (510 mm).

5. For straight shaping, guide the work along a _____.

6. Depth collars should be used when doing _____ shaping.

7. A pair of matched cutters are needed when making _____-and-groove joints.

8. When shaping a straight edge, position the _____ for depth of cut.

9. Shaping can be done on a drill press, provided speeds of at least _____ RPM can be obtained.

10. Shaper cutters come in many shapes. T or F

11. A depth collar is sometimes used to limit depth of cut. T or F

12. For shaping the entire edge of a piece of stock, use a _____, which rides against the collar.

13. Name these common parts of the shaper. Fig. 38-1:

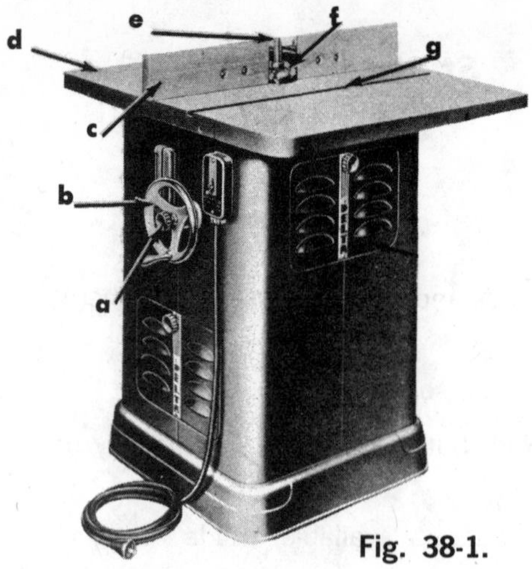

Fig. 38-1.

a. _____
b. _____
c. _____
d. _____
e. _____
f. _____
g. _____

14. When shaping all edges and ends of stock, the first cut should be across the _____ _____.

15. When using a depth collar for limiting the depth of cut, the collar *cannot* be located: (a) above the cutter, (b) below the cutter, (c) below the table, (d) between the cutters.

16. When using a fence to guide the work and the entire edge of the work is removed, the rear fence must be in line with the front fence. T or F

17. The feed direction is determined by the direction of rotation of the cutter. T or F

18. The material being shaped must be: (a) square, (b) clamped to the table, (c) free of knots, (d) straight.

19. Check the spelling of the following words. If correct, place a ''C'' in the space. If incorrect, give the correct spelling.

a. Rotation

b. Spindel

c. Cutter

d. Toungue

_____

_____

_____

_____

Study Guide No. 39
MORTISER

Reviewing the Main Ideas

1. The mortiser is used to cut the rectangular opening that is one part of the _____-and-tenon joint.

2. The vertical hollow-chisel _____ is used in most small shops.

3. For sash-and-door manufacturers, a _____ mortiser is commonly used. In large furniture manufacturing, a horizontal, multiple spindle mortiser is employed.

4. The square hole cut by a mortiser is made by combining a bit which bores the round hole and a square _____ which squares out the corners.

5. A mortiser will never cut a square, clean hole all the way to the bottom of the opening. For this reason it is common practice to make the _____ about 1/8 inch (3 mm) shorter than the mortise.

6. A mortising attachment can be used on the _____ _____.

Checking Your Knowledge

1. For a 3/4-inch (19 mm) chisel, the bit should extend beyond the chisel by an amount of: (a) 1/64″ (0.5 mm), (b) 1/32″ (1 mm), (c) 1/16″ (1.6 mm), (d) 1/4″ (6.4 mm).

2. You should center the chisel before making final passes when cutting an oblong mortise. T or F

3. A sash-and-door manufacturer would use a _____ mortiser.

4. The mortiser shown in the text in Fig. 39-3 cuts a square with a rounded bottom. T or F

5. On most mortisers, the table can move in: (a) one direction, (b) two directions, (c) three directions, (d) four directions.

6. In cutting mortises, all identical mortises should be cut at the same time. T or F

7. In adjusting a mortising chisel, make sure it touches the table at the bottom of the stroke. T or F

8. Fig. 39-10a in the text shows a _____ attachment for the drill press.

9. As shown in Fig. 39-7 in the text, the mortising chisel gets rid of the shaving through the chisel opening in the: (a) bottom, (b) top, (c) four sides, (d) one side.

10. The chisel must be aligned by holding a square against the side of it and the fence. T or F

11. Before cutting a mortise, the work should be securely clamped. T or F

12. Check the spelling of the following words. If correct, place a "C" in the space. If incorrect, give the correct spelling.

a. Mortiser _____

b. Chissel _____

c. Attachment _____

d. Cleareance _____

Study Guide No. 40
POWER DRILLING AND BORING

Reviewing the Main Ideas

1. In the furniture industry, a _____ machine is frequently used for making dowel holes, which is a precision operation.

2. There are both vertical and _____ spindle boring machines.

3. High-speed steel _____, which may be used on metal or wood, are available in many diameters.

4. For general work in both metal and wood, the _____ drill should have an included angle of 118 degrees.

5. An auger bit for power drill should have a _____ shank and a brad point.

6. Masonry drills with carbide tips should be used at _____ speeds and with heavy pressure.

7. A plug cutter makes matching wood plugs to conceal _____ heads.

8. The _____ bit bores in end grains, through knots, and in cross-grain.

9. Two-speed electric drills can be used at high speed for wood and plastic, or at lower speed for _____.

10. On the drill press, speeds of 1200 to _____ RPM should be used for drilling and boring wood.

Checking Your Knowledge

1. The device used in the furniture industry for boring holes is either the _____ or _____ spindle boring machine.

2. Power drilling of holes in school shops is done most commonly with a portable electric drill, or a _____ _____.

3. The size of a drill press is indicated by the largest diameter of stock through which a hole can be drilled. T or F

4. For drilling and boring wood, use speeds of _____ to _____ RPM.

5. Work can be held in place with the hand in most drilling and boring of small holes. T or F

6. The shanks of all bits or drills used in a portable drill should be _____.

7. To bore flat bottom holes use a _____ bit.

8. The size of a portable electric drill is usually indicated by the diameter of drill or bit that it will hold. T or F

_____

9. Wooden plugs are used to cover screw heads. T or F

_____

10. Identify these common cutting tools. Fig. 40-1:

a. _____

b. _____

c. _____

d. _____

e. _____

f. _____

g. _____

h. _____

i. _____

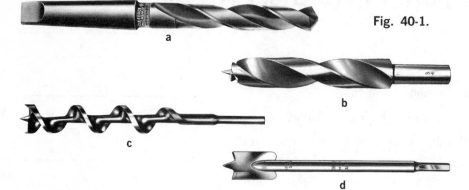
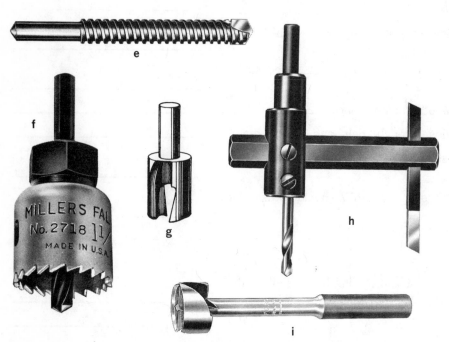

Fig. 40-1.

11. Fig. 40-16 in the text shows the drilling of dowel holes for a _____ joint.

_____

12. The included angle for an all-purpose twist drill should be _____ degrees.

_____

13. A spur machine bit looks like a combination of a twist drill and a Foerstner bit. T or F

_____

14. Portable electric drills that operate without 110-volt electricity are available. T or F

_____

15. An 18-inch (460 mm) drill press measures _____ (millimetres) from the center of the chuck to the column.

_____

16. A cutting tool used at slow speed and with heavy pressure is the _____ drill with carbide tip.

_____

17. Check the spelling of the following words. If correct, place a "C" in the space. If incorrect, give the correct spelling.

   a. Forstner   _____

   b. Variable speed   _____

   c. Multeple spindle   _____

Name_____

Score_____

Study Guide No. 41
WOOD LATHE

Reviewing the Main Ideas

1. The wood lathe combines _____ with the ability to perform delicate operations.

_____

2. The skilled cabinetmaker and the _____ are among the workers in industry who should be able to use the lathe.

_____

3. Lathe size is designated by the largest _____ of stock it will turn and the bed length.

_____

4. Several kinds of turning tools, including the gouge, skew, roundnose, spear point and _____ tool, can be used for various types of turning.

_____

5. The two basic methods of turning are scraping and _____, or paring.

_____

6. Spindle _____ is done with the work held between centers.

_____

Checking Your Knowledge

1. Name the parts of the lathe. Fig. 41-1:

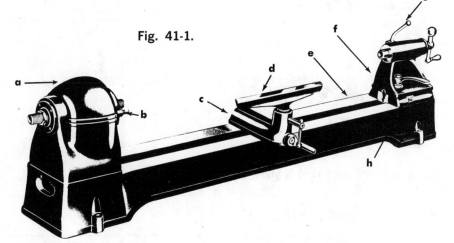

Fig. 41-1.

a. _____

b. _____

c. _____

d. _____

e. _____

f. _____

g. _____

h. _____

2. Speeds of about _____ RPM should be used for faceplate work.

_____

3. The two basic methods of turning are the _____ method and the _____ method.

_____

_____

4. The patternmaker uses the _____ method.

_____

5. The tool rest should clear the stock by about 1/8 inch (3 mm). T or F

_____

6. Rough cutting is done with a gouge. T or F

_____

7. Identify these common measuring and marking tools. Fig. 41-2:

a. _____
b. _____
c. _____
d. _____
e. _____

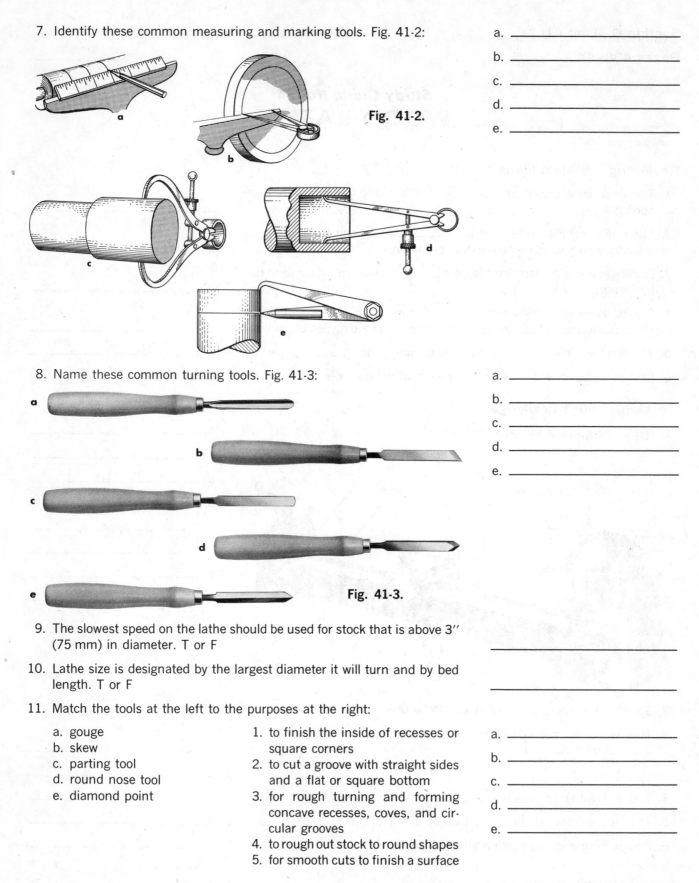

Fig. 41-2.

8. Name these common turning tools. Fig. 41-3:

a. _____
b. _____
c. _____
d. _____
e. _____

Fig. 41-3.

9. The slowest speed on the lathe should be used for stock that is above 3″ (75 mm) in diameter. T or F

_____

10. Lathe size is designated by the largest diameter it will turn and by bed length. T or F

_____

11. Match the tools at the left to the purposes at the right:

a. gouge
b. skew
c. parting tool
d. round nose tool
e. diamond point

1. to finish the inside of recesses or square corners
2. to cut a groove with straight sides and a flat or square bottom
3. for rough turning and forming concave recesses, coves, and circular grooves
4. to rough out stock to round shapes
5. for smooth cuts to finish a surface

a. _____
b. _____
c. _____
d. _____
e. _____

136

12. When turning stock that is from 1 to 2 inches (25 to 50 mm) in diameter, use the _____ speed.

      _____

13. Rough turning should be done to about _____ (inches) over finished diameter.

      _____

14. Faceplate turning is done by the _____ method.

      _____

15. Fig. 41-14 in the text shows the use of a skew for scraping. T or F

      _____

16. Fig. 41-17a in the text shows the use of a round nose tool for cutting concave surfaces. T or F

      _____

17. The following turning tool would be used to make a narrow cut to a given diameter: (a) skew, (b) gouge, (c) parting tool, (d) diamond point.

      _____

18. In spindle turning between centers, the work is driven by a: (a) live center, (b) dead center, (c) tool rest, (d) tool stock.

      _____

19. The dead center is held in the: (a) tailstock, (b) headstock, (c) tool post, (d) cross slide.

      _____

20. In doing faceplate turning, the work is held between centers. T or F

21. When turning hardwood, saw diagonals across the corners to help turn the wood. T or F

      _____

22. One of the following is *not* a term commonly used for the center that turns the work when turning between centers: (a) drive center, (b) spur center, (c) live center, (d) main center.

      _____

23. Identify these three types of faceplates. Fig. 41-4:

a. _____

b. _____

c. _____

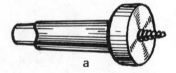

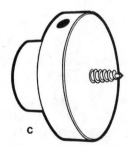

Fig. 41-4.

24. The following turning tool is used to rough out stock: (a) gouge, (b) spear point, (c) round nose, (d) parting tool.

      _____

25. Before starting the wood lathe, you should turn the stock one or two revolutions by _____.

      _____

26. Check the spelling of the following words. If correct, place a "C" in the
space. If incorrect, give the correct spelling.

    a. Automatic   _____

    b. Hermaphrodete   _____

    c. Skeu   _____

    d. Diamond   _____

Name_____

Score_____

Study Guide No. 42
JOINERY

Reviewing the Main Ideas

1. Joints are used to assemble and _____ together two or more pieces of wood.

2. Over 100 kinds of wood _____ are used in house construction.

3. Most joints are permanently fastened with glue, nails, and/or _____.

4. A _____ is a pin or peg that fits into two matching holes to strengthen a joint.

5. A key is often placed across the corner of a _____ joint.

6. The easiest and simplest joint to use is the _____ joint.

7. A groove cut across grain to receive the butt end of a second piece is a _____.

8. An efficient method of constructing _____ shapes is by the V-fold miter system.

9. V-grooving is done in industry on a _____.

_____

_____

_____

_____

_____

_____

_____

_____

Checking Your Knowledge

1. Any variation from a true or plane surface is called _____.

2. Always plane a board with the grain. T or F

3. There are over 100 varieties of joints but most of them are adaptations of _____ (number) basic types.

4. A good rule to follow is to choose the simplest joint that will do the job. T or F

_____

_____

_____

_____

5. Match the items at the left to the purposes at the right:

   a. corner block
   b. dowel
   c. gussets
   d. spline
   e. key
   f. glue block

   1. a thin piece of wood or metal inserted in a groove between two parts of a joint
   2. a pin or peg of wood
   3. a small piece of wood inserted in one or both parts of a joint to hold it firmly together
   4. small triangular-shaped pieces of wood used to strengthen two adjoining surfaces
   5. large triangular pieces which add strength at the corners of frames
   6. triangular or trapezoid shapes used in truss roof framing

   a. _____
   b. _____
   c. _____
   d. _____
   e. _____
   f. _____

6. A butt joint is simple to make. T or F

7. Identify these common end joints. Fig. 42-1:

a. _____

b. _____

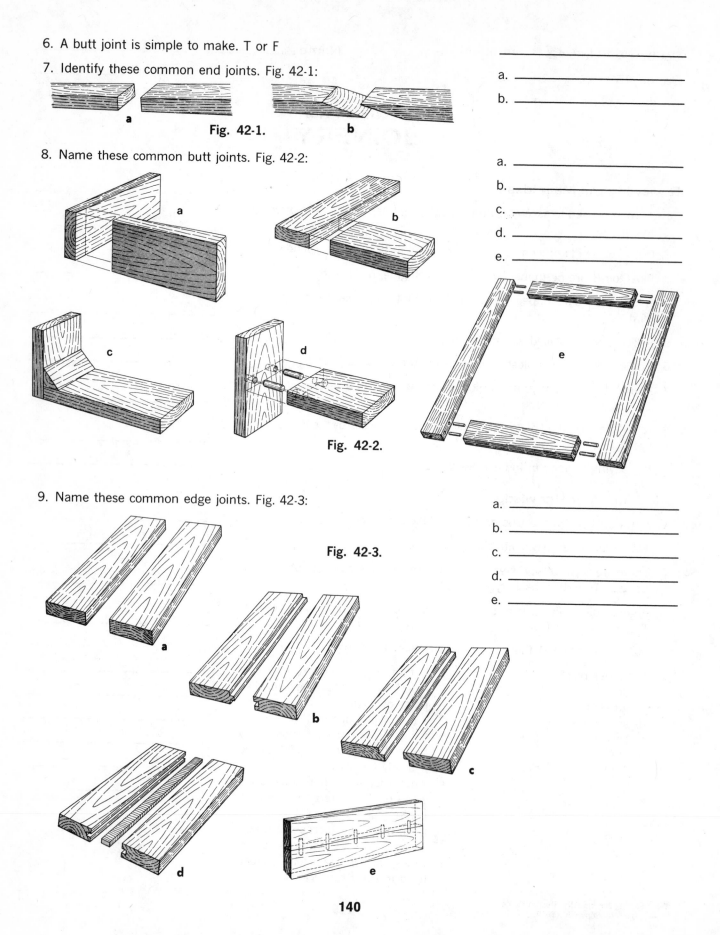

Fig. 42-1.

8. Name these common butt joints. Fig. 42-2:

a. _____
b. _____
c. _____
d. _____
e. _____

Fig. 42-2.

9. Name these common edge joints. Fig. 42-3:

a. _____
b. _____
c. _____
d. _____
e. _____

Fig. 42-3.

10. Identify these dado joints. Fig. 42-4:

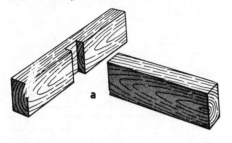
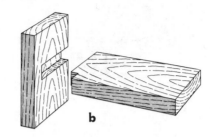
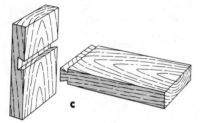
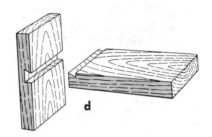

a. _____

b. _____

c. _____

d. _____

e. _____

Fig. 42-4.

11. Name these lap joints. Fig. 42-5:

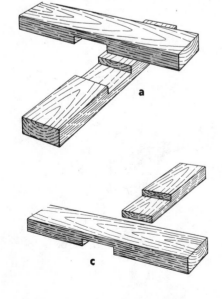

a. _____

b. _____

c. _____

d. _____

Fig. 42-5.

12. Name these miter joints. Fig. 42-6:

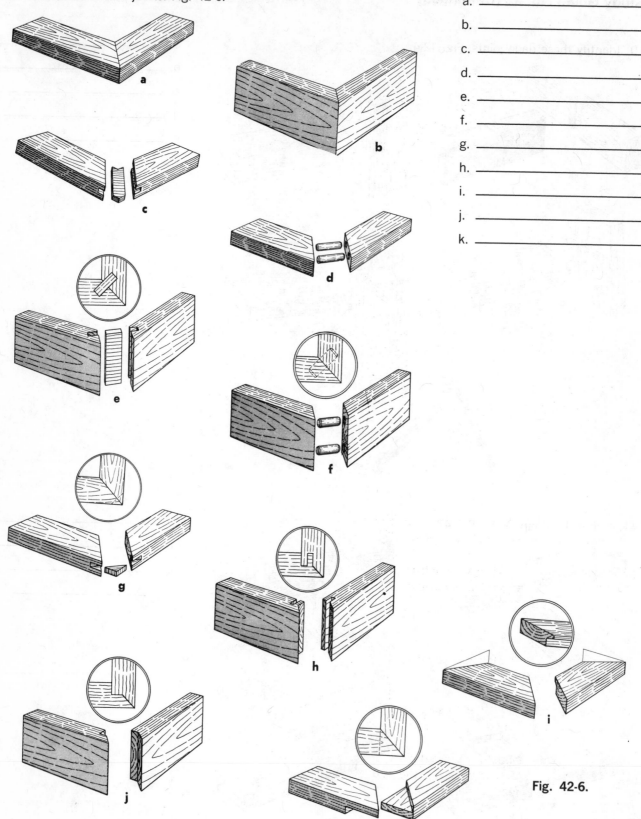

a. _____
b. _____
c. _____
d. _____
e. _____
f. _____
g. _____
h. _____
i. _____
j. _____
k. _____

Fig. 42-6.

142

13. Identify these mortise-and-tenon joints. Fig. 42-7:

a. _____
b. _____
c. _____
d. _____

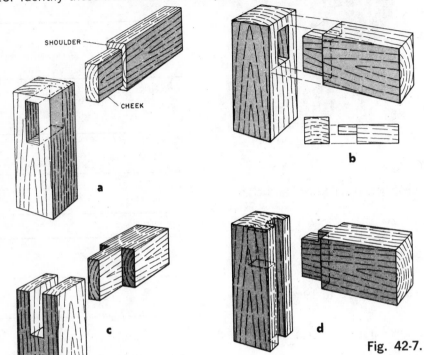

Fig. 42-7.

14. Name these dovetail joints. Fig. 42-8:

a. _____
b. _____

15. The most important end joint for industrial use is the _____ joint.

16. Homes built of single-wall construction use a _____-and-_____ joint to join the pieces together.

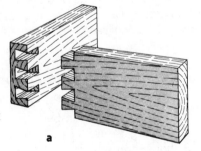

a

_____

_____

17. A good joint for installing shelves is the _____ joint.

18. A blind dado is often called a _____.

19. In a dado-and-rabbet joint, the dado is cut to _____ the thickness of the stock and to a depth equal to 1/2 to _____ the thickness.

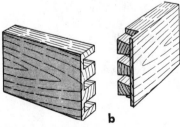

b

Fig. 42-8.

_____

_____

_____

_____

Woodworking for Industry Student Guide
John L. Feirer—Copyright © 1979

20. The joint shown in Fig. 42-9 is strengthened with a _____.

21. A joint commonly used in making window frames and screen doors is the _____ _____ joint.

22. The miter joint is sometimes rather weak unless strengthened with dowels, a spline, or a key. T or F

23. Most miter joints are cut in an angle of _____ degrees to form a 90-degree corner.

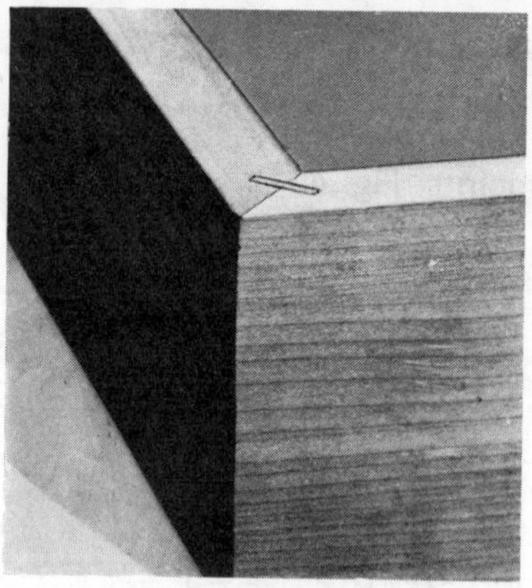

24. Another name for the compound miter joint is the _____ joint.

Fig. 42-9.

25. A good joint to use in leg-and-rail construction for tables and chairs is called a _____-and-_____ joint.

26. The tenon of a mortise-and-tenon joint should be cut at about _____ the thickness of the stock.

27. A tenon should be cut about 1/2 to 3/4 inch (13 to 19 mm) narrower than the total width of the stock. T or F

28. A joint found in the finest quality drawer-and-box construction is called the _____.

29. The best way to cut the mortise of a dovetail-dado joint is to install a dovetail bit on a _____ or drill press.

30. If a compound miter joint is to be made with a four-side butt and the tilt of the work is to be 25 degrees, the blade should be tilted to _____ degrees and the miter gauge set to _____ degrees.

31. Match the kinds of joints listed at the left to the common uses of joints at the right:

a. end lap joint
b. butt joint
c. mortise-and-tenon joint
d. tongue-and-groove joint
e. finger joint
f. dado joint
g. dovetail joint
h. miter joint
i. rabbet joint

1. spliced 2″ x 4″ lumber
2. flooring
3. house framing
4. simple box
5. cabinet shelves
6. screen doors
7. picture frame
8. table
9. best drawer construction

a. _____
b. _____
c. _____
d. _____
e. _____
f. _____
g. _____
h. _____
i. _____

32. A good joint for fastening drawer fronts to sides is: (a) butt, (b) miter, (c) dovetail, (d) mortise-and-tenon.

144

33. Check the spelling of the following words. If correct, place a "C" in the
    space. If incorrect, give the correct spelling.

    a. Jointery   _____

    b. Gusset   _____

    c. Scarfe   _____

    d. Tongue-and-groove   _____

Study Guide No. 43
ADHESIVES AND GLUING

Reviewing the Main Ideas

1. Any _____, cement, or mucilage used to bond materials together is called an adhesive.

_____

2. Common problems in gluing include recognizing the _____ of wood, gluing end grain, moisture content, well-fitted joints, gap-filling properties of glues, method of applying, curing qualities, and machined surfaces.

_____

3. Wood can be glued more easily than other materials because of its _____ structure.

_____

4. Many types of _____ devices can be used to hold glued-up parts together while glue sets.

_____

5. Some of the more common types of clamps are the _____ screw, the C-clamp, and the bar or cabinet clamp.

_____

6. In industry, many special clamping tools are used, including continuous and batch _____.

_____

7. Steps in gluing include mixing and spreading the glue, _____ the parts, applying pressure, curing, and checking the glue joints.

_____

8. Two common types of rubber-base adhesives are the mastics (elastomeric construction adhesives) and the _____ adhesives.

_____

Checking Your Knowledge

1. Any glue, cement, or mucilage that bonds material together is called an _____.

_____

2. The most difficult kind of gluing is: (a) edge, (b) face, (c) end, (d) scarf.

_____

3. Match the items at the left to those at the right (see text Fig. 43-20):

a. animal
b. polyvinyl acetate
c. resorcinol resin
d. urea resin
e. casein
f. contact adhesive
g. epoxy resins

1. marketed only as liquid, ready to use
2. furniture assembly; use is declining
3. very resistant to moisture and damp conditions; dark red
4. not suitable for exterior uses
5. for bonding metals, certain plastics, and some masonry
6. high in both wet and dry strength; moderately durable under damp conditions
7. on-the-job bonding of decorative tops to kitchen counters

a. _____
b. _____
c. _____
d. _____
e. _____
f. _____
g. _____

4. A number 4/0 handscrew has jaws that are _____ (millimetres) long.   _____

5. Identify the clamps for gluing shown in Fig. 43-1:   a. _____

b. _____

Fig. 43-1.

c. _____

a

b

c

6. It is necessary to use clamping blocks with hand screws. T or F   _____

7. The glue that comes in two separate containers and must be mixed before using is _____ glue.   _____

8. Most types of phenol resin require hot _____ at about 260 to 300 °F (127 to 150 °C).   _____

9. Epoxy resins are marketed in two parts, resin and _____ agent.   _____

10. When gluing stock edge to edge, alternate the clamps, one from one side and the next from the opposite side. T or F _____

11. Animal adhesive has high dry strength but low resistance to _____. _____

12. Glue made from milk curd is called _____ glue. _____

13. The best glue to use for a completely waterproof job is: (a) animal, (b) casein, (c) resorcinol, (d) fish. _____

14. A good method of removing glue is to cut it off on a planer or jointer. T or F _____

15. Wood surfaces to be glued may first be sanded. T or F _____

16. Plywood surfaces may be sanded before gluing. T or F _____

17. There are _____ important "keys" that make for a good glue joint. _____

18. The average moisture content of interior woodwork is about _____ percent for the United States. _____

19. The moisture content of interior woodwork is higher along the coast in the summer than in the northern states in winter. T or F _____

20. Glues must penetrate the cell walls of wood to provide a good glue joint. T or F _____

21. A poor glue joint will result if stock has been given a burnished surface as it goes through a planer or jointer. T or F _____

22. When gluing plywood surfaces together, it is sometimes necessary to sand lightly because the plywood has a glazed surface. T or F _____

23. In end gluing, the pores tend to absorb the glue. T or F _____

24. When mixing powdered glues, always mix more than can be used. T or F _____

25. When glue is spread only on one surface of stock, it is called _____ _____. _____

26. When gluing edge to edge, clamps should be placed every _____ to _____ (inches). _____

_____

27. Identify these common types of joints that require gluing. Fig. 43-2:

a. _____

Fig. 43-2.   b. _____

c. _____

d. _____

e. _____

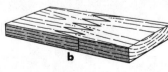

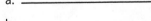
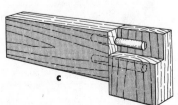
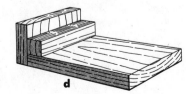

28. A joint that has too little glue, resulting in a weak glue joint, is called a
_____ joint.

29. A joint in which the glue has become jelly at the glue line is called a
_____ joint.

30. A joint in which the glue has dried without bonding at the glue line is
called a _____ joint.

31. When a bar clamp has been tightened hard with one hand, the clamp will
develop _____ to _____ pounds pressure.

32. In industry, the curing of glue can be speeded by the use of hot presses or
high-frequency heat. T or F

33. When gluing up stock, the moisture content should not vary more than
_____ percent.

34. Check the spelling of the following words. If correct, place a "C" in the
space. If incorrect, give the correct spelling.

a. Glueing

b. Continuous

c. Syntheatic

d. Resorsinol

e. Epoxy resin

Section E—Unit 44

Pages 498–519

Name ______________

Score ______________

Study Guide No. 44

WOOD FASTENERS

Reviewing the Main Ideas

1. The strength and stability of many wood products depend upon ______ fasteners. ______________
2. A wide ______ of fasteners, such as nails, screws, bolts, and pins, can be used with wood. ______________
3. Some common nailing tools are the claw hammer, nail set, stapling tools, and nailing ______. ______________
4. General-purpose nails include the common, ______, casing, and finishing varieties. ______________
5. Flooring nails have a cement-coated surface or a spiral or ______ thread. ______________
6. The two common methods of nailing in building construction are straight driving and ______. ______________
7. Splitting occurs much more rapidly on ______ woods than on lighter woods. ______________
8. Common head shapes of screws are flat, ______, and oval. ______________
9. Plain and spiral type describe two common varieties of ______. ______________
10. Common fasteners for attaching cabinets and other items to walls include toggle bolts, molly bolts, anchor bolts, rawl plugs, and ______ anchors. ______________
11. Fasteners larger than common wire nails are common wire ______. ______________
12. Staples are available in clips or ______ for use in power staplers. ______________

Checking Your Knowledge

1. Identify these types of general-purpose nails. Fig. 44-1:

a. ______________
b. ______________
c. ______________
d. ______________

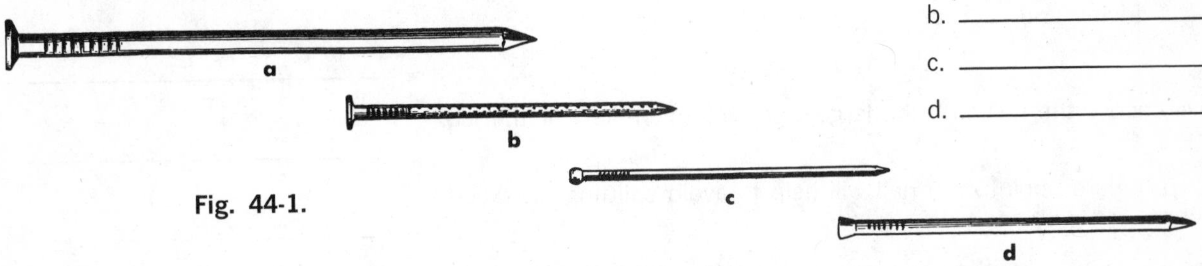

Fig. 44-1.

2. The tool used to drive the head of a nail below the surface is called a ______ ______. ______________
3. The size "3d" refers to: (a) sandpaper, (b) corrugated fasteners, (c) nails, (d) screws. ______________

4. Name these common tools used in assembly. Fig. 44-2:

a. _____

b. _____

Fig. 44-2.

5. Common nails are set with a nail set. T or F

_____

6. The 5d finishing nail is larger in diameter than the 5d common nail. T or F

_____

7. A 40d nail is _____ inches long.

_____

8. Name these special purpose nails. Fig. 44-3:

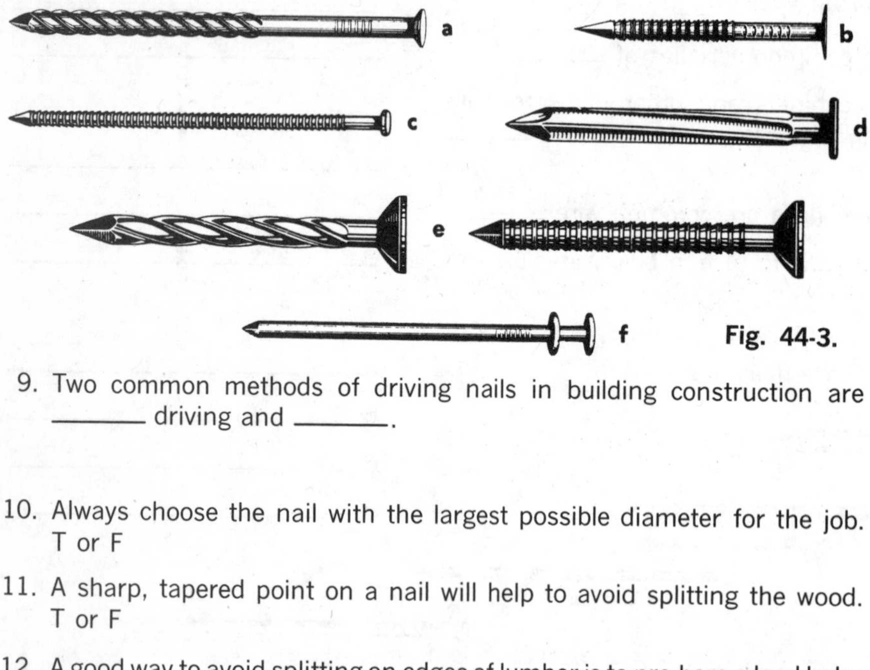

Fig. 44-3.

a. _____

b. _____

c. _____

d. _____

e. _____

f. _____

9. Two common methods of driving nails in building construction are _____ driving and _____.

_____

_____

10. Always choose the nail with the largest possible diameter for the job. T or F

_____

11. A sharp, tapered point on a nail will help to avoid splitting the wood. T or F

_____

12. A good way to avoid splitting on edges of lumber is to pre-bore a lead hole. T or F

_____

13. Splitting occurs more rapidly on lighter weight woods than on denser woods. T or F

_____

14. The extra holding power of cement-coated nails is permanent. T or F

_____

15. To have equal withdrawal strength, aluminum nails must be larger in diameter than steel nails. T or F

_____

16. The correct size finishing nail for 5/8-inch plywood is a _____ or _____ .

_____

_____

17. Identify these common types of wood screws. Fig. 44-4:

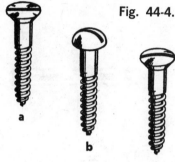

Fig. 44-4.

a. _____

b. _____

c. _____

18. One of the following is *not* a material used in wood screws: (a) mild steel, (b) aluminum, (c) nickel silver, (d) copper.

_____

19. Flathead screws of mild steel are made with a blue finish. T or F

_____

20. A 20-gauge screw is _____ inches long.

_____

21. It is good practice to clinch a nail with the grain. T or F

_____

22. A flathead screw is countersunk to be flush with the surface. T or F

_____

23. The correct twist drill to use for the shank-clearance hole for a No. 4 screw is _____ (millimetres).

_____

24. The countersink used to install flathead screws should be a _____-degree countersink.

_____

25. For withdrawal loads, the pilot hole should be slightly less than _____ percent of the threaded portion.

_____

26. Choose a screw long enough to go _____ its length into the second part.

_____

27. A good size screw to use with 1/2-inch (13 mm) plywood is a No. _____ that is _____ (inches) long.

_____

_____

28. Identify these heavy screws and bolts. Fig. 44-5:

a. _____

b. _____

c. _____

d. _____

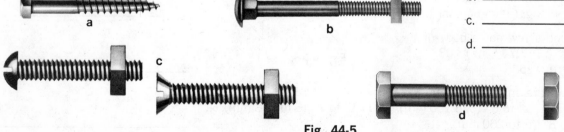

Fig. 44-5.

29. Identify these common wall fasteners. Fig. 44-6:

a. _____

b. _____

c. _____

d. _____

e. _____

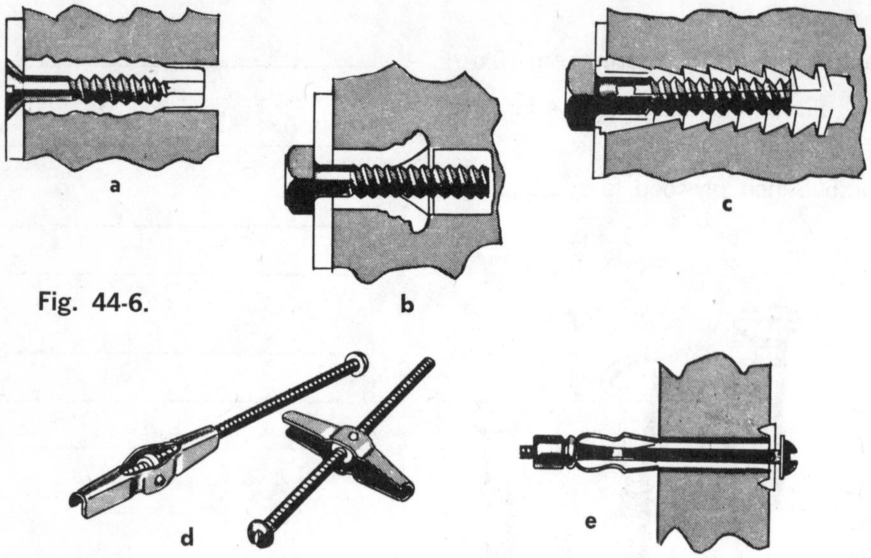

Fig. 44-6.

30. Name these common household fasteners. Fig. 44-7:

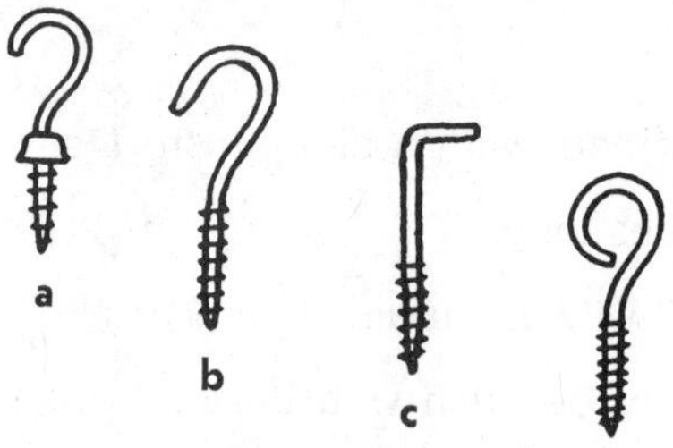

a. _____

b. _____

c. _____

d. _____

Fig. 44-7.

31. Identify these common repair plates. Fig. 44-8:

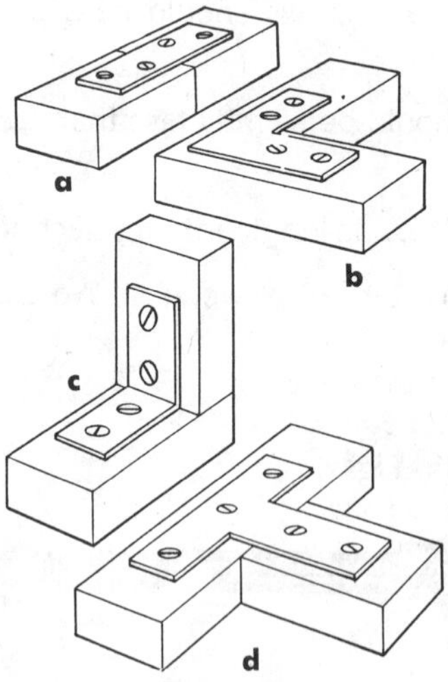

a. _____

b. _____

c. _____

d. _____

32. The length of a 10d nail is: (a) 1 1/2'', (b) 2'', (c) 2 1/2'', (d) 3''.

33. The head of a common nail is: (a) flat, (b) round, (c) oval, (d) concave.

34. Casing nails are not recommended for: (a) door frames, (b) cornices, (c) rough framing, (d) cornerboards.

35. A No. 3 wood screw has a body diameter of: (a) .073'', (b) .083'', (c) .099'', (d) .125''.

Fig. 44-8.

36. Wood screws are made in lengths as follows: (a) 1/4'' to 4'' (6 to 100 mm), (b) 1/4'' to 6'' (6 to 150 mm), (c) 1/4'' to 7'' (6 to 178 mm), (d) 1/4'' to 8'' (6 to 200 mm).

_____

_____

_____

_____

_____

37. Screws used for attaching hardware usually have: (a) flat heads, (b) round heads, (c) oval heads, (d) Phillips heads.

_____

38. The correct shank clearance hole for a No. 8 wood screw is _____ (inches).

_____

39. A 4d box nail is larger in diameter than a 4d finishing nail. T or F

_____

40. The correct size finishing nail to choose for 5/8-inch plywood is: (a) 3d, (b) 4d, (c) 8d, (d) 10d.

_____

41. Give the diameter in thousandths of an inch of a No. 9 wood screw.

_____

42. The shank diameter of a No. 10 screw is _____ thousandths of an inch larger than a No. 4 screw.

_____

43. When installing bolts in a vertical piece of lumber, the holes should be located at least _____ times the diameter of the bolt from the edge.

_____

44. The auger-bit size for a plug hole for a No. 7 wood screw is a number _____.

_____

45. Give the diameter in thousandths of an inch of a gauge No. 9 nail.

_____

46. Wood screws 1/2 inch long are available in shank sizes from number _____ to _____.

_____

_____

47. Check the spelling of the following words. If correct, place a "C" in the space. If incorrect, give the correct spelling.

  a. Pilot

_____

  b. Essutcheon

_____

  c. Stapeling

_____

Name _____

Score _____

Study Guide No. 45
LAMINATING AND BENDING

Reviewing the Main Ideas

1. Laminating is a process of gluing two or more layers of wood together with the grain approximately _____.

   _____

2. There are many advantages in glued, _____ wood members, including better use of materials and the possibility for larger units of wood.

   _____

3. Bending is done both on _____ lumber and in laminated construction.

   _____

4. In bending solid wood, the material needs to be steamed or soaked until it contains 20 to 25 percent _____.

   _____

5. Bent, laminated pieces can be produced without moisture by _____ several thin layers of material together.

   _____

6. Bending can provide a variety of functional and attractive _____ members.

   _____

7. The term curved or _____ plywood refers to plywood that is glued to the desired shape.

   _____

Checking Your Knowledge

1. Gluing two or more layers of wood together with the grain approximately parallel is called _____.

   _____

2. One of the following is *not* an advantage of laminated wood construction: (a) the best material can be used for maximum strength, (b) material with checks and other defects can be used, (c) smaller pieces of lumber can be utilized, (d) complex shapes can be produced.

   _____

3. The dimension and length of glued, laminated arches and beams is quite limited. T or F

   _____

4. In constructing laminated wood members, the material should have no more than _____ percent variation in moisture content.

   _____

5. Two most commonly used woods for laminating beams and arches are Douglas fir and _____ _____.

   _____

6. One method of forming curved parts is by cutting from solid stock. T or F

   _____

7. One of the following is *not* among the best materials for bending curved parts for furniture: (a) elm, (b) hickory, (c) ash, (d) pine.

   _____

8. When bending 3/4-inch (19 mm) squares on a 20-inch (508 mm) radius, the percentage of breakage of ash is approximately _____ percent.

9. To bend solid wood, it must be steamed or soaked until it contains from _____ to _____ percent moisture.

_____

_____

10. Dry wood to be bent should be steamed or soaked about _____ hour(s) for each inch of thickness.

_____

11. Laminated wood is to _____ grain as plywood is to right-angle grain.

_____

12. When bending skies on which glue must be used, always apply good hide glue. T or F

_____

13. In bending, the interior of wood can be compressed by as much as _____ percent.

_____

14. Laminated structures are subject to less shrinking and checking than are pieces of solid lumber. T or F

_____

15. Laminated beams are usually made from material up to _____ (inches) in thickness.

_____

16. Identify these common types of laminated beams. Fig. 45-1:

a. _____

b. _____

c. _____

d. _____

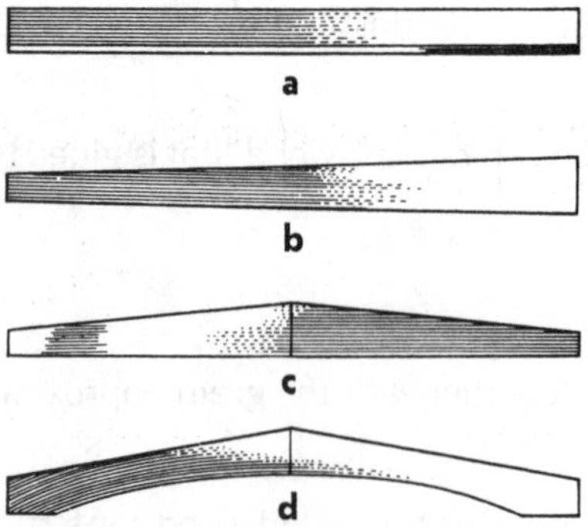

Fig. 45-1.

17. A high V-type arch is used in the framework of the church shown in the text in Fig. 45-3. T or F

_____

18. Of the following, the most common joint used to join the ends of stock in laminated construction is the: (a) rabbet joint, (b) finger joint, (c) dado joint, (d) dovetail joint.

_____

19. In bending solid wood, the exterior of the wood can be stretched about: (a) less than 2 percent, (b) 10 to 11 percent, (c) 5 to 6 percent, (d) 14 to 15 percent.

_____

20. Name these three types of arches. Fig. 45-2:

a. _____

b. _____

c. _____

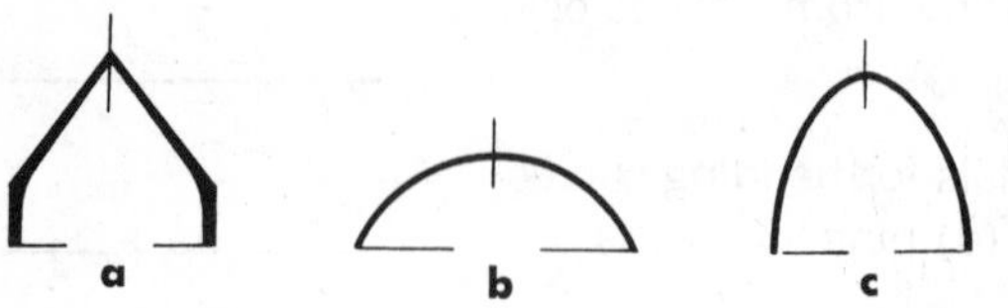

Fig. 45-2.

21. Identify these common kinds of breaks. Fig. 45-3:

a. _____

b. _____

c. _____

d. _____

22. When 3/4-inch (19 mm) squares of the following woods are bent on a 20-inch (508 mm) radius, the one with the largest percentage of breakage is: (a) beech, (b) cottonwood, (c) birch, (d) elm.

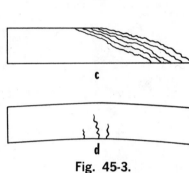

Fig. 45-3.

_____

23. When bending dry material, cut or plane it to a thickness of _____ or _____ (millimetres).

_____

_____

24. Woods for bending do *not* include: (a) white oak, (b) hickory, (c) basswood, (d) ash.

_____

25. Check the spelling of the following words. If correct, place a "C" in the space. If incorrect, give the correct spelling.

a. Fabricate

_____

b. Parobolic

_____

c. Breakage

_____

Study Guide No. 46
ABRASIVES AND SANDING

Reviewing the Main Ideas

1. Sanding is classified in three ways: sanding before finishing, sanding of _____ coats, and wet sanding of finish coats.

   _____

2. Five common kinds of material used for coated abrasives are flint, emery, garnet, aluminum oxide, and _____ _____.

   _____

3. All coated abrasives consist of an abrasive (mineral), a backing (paper, cloth, or combination), a _____, and a coating.

   _____

4. The abrasive silicon carbide approaches the _____ in hardness.

   _____

5. Aluminum oxide is more durable and less _____ than silicon carbide.

   _____

6. The three ways of applying abrasives to the bonds are closed coat, open coat, and _____.

   _____

7. Rough sanding removes knife marks and smooths torn grain. Finish sanding and polishing are done to remove very fine _____, all of which are parallel to the grain.

   _____

8. Abrasives are made in the form of sheets, rolls, disks, and _____.

   _____

9. Common sanding machines are the belt and disk sander, the belt sander with a hand stroke or power stroke, spindle sanders, and several types of _____ sanders.

   _____

Checking Your Knowledge

1. Sandpaper is a good substitute for a plane. T or F

   _____

2. Flint paper is harder and sharper than garnet paper. T or F

   _____

3. Another name for flint is _____.

   _____

4. Extra coarse garnet paper is recommended for use on metal. T or F

   _____

5. One of the following is *not* a natural abrasive: (a) flint, (b) emery, (c) silicon carbide, (d) garnet.

   _____

6. When sanding a curved surface, always use a machine. T or F

   _____

7. The common diameters of coated abrasives for disk sanders are _____ and _____ (inches).

   _____

   _____

8. When hand sanding, always sand across the grain. T or F

   _____

9. One of the following is *not* a common backing for abrasives: (a) paper, (b) cloth, (c) fiber, (d) plastics.

10. There are two bond layers used in locking the abrasive to the backing; the first is called the _____ coat and the second is called the _____ coat.

11. Animal-hide glue can be used for both of the bond layers for abrasives. T or F

12. Grit sizes get finer as the number goes up. T or F

13. Name the parts of a disk sander. Fig. 46-1:

Fig. 46-1.

14. Name the parts of a belt sander. Fig. 46-2:

15. A No. 30 garnet paper is the same as a 2 1/2 garnet paper. T or F

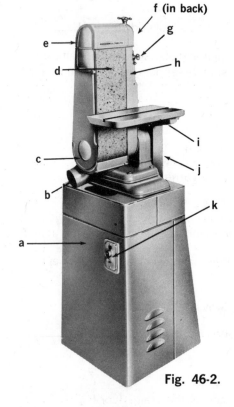

Fig. 46-2.

_____

_____
_____

_____

_____

a. _____
b. _____
c. _____
d. _____
e. _____
f. _____
g. _____

a. _____
b. _____
c. _____
d. _____
e. _____
f. _____
g. _____
h. _____
i. _____
j. _____
k. _____

_____

16. The standard size for garnet paper is 9″ x 11″ (229 x 279 mm). T or F   _____

17. End grain is sanded in one direction only. T or F   _____

18. Identify these three principal methods of sanding with the finishing sander. Fig. 46-3:

a. _____

b. _____

c. _____

a   b   c

Fig. 46-3.

19. Many cutting operations should be done after sanding. T or F   _____

20. Guide the portable belt sander with a "skimming motion." T or F   _____

21. The standard size for garnet sandpaper sheets is: (a) 8″ x 10″ (203 x 254 mm), (b) 9″ x 11″ (229 x 279 mm), (c) 10″ x 12″ (254 x 305 mm), (d) 10″ x 15″ (254 x 381 mm).   _____

22. A medium-grade sandpaper with a grit number of 100 is equivalent to: (a) 1/2, (b) 2/0, (c) 4/0, (d) 7/0.   _____

23. Sheet size of flint paper is the same as all other coated abrasives. T or F   _____

24. The letters A, B, C, and D after the grit sizes indicate the weight of the backing. T or F   _____

25. Select the coarsest coated abrasive paper: (a) 30, (b) 1 1/2, (c) 1/2, (d) 100.   _____

26. Abrasives are *not* made in one of the following forms: (a) sheets, (b) rolls, (c) spheres, (d) belts.   _____

27. Fiber has more body than other coated abrasive backings. T or F   _____

28. Tear a piece of 9″ x 11″ (229 x 279 mm) abrasive paper in half the long way. Tear each half into two equal-sized pieces. The size of each piece is _____ x _____ (millimetres).   _____

29. An orange to deep red material of medium hardness used for a coated abrasive is called _____.   _____

30. Check the spelling of the following words. If correct, place a "C" in the space. If incorrect, give the correct spelling.

    a. Garenet   _____

    b. Sylicone carbide   _____

    c. Orbiatal   _____

Name_____

Score_____

Study Guide No. 47
INSTALLING HARDWARE

Reviewing the Main Ideas

1. The quality of a home or a piece of furniture greatly depends on its _____.

2. Common kinds of hardware include hinges, handles, pulls, catches, and _____.

3. Decorative hardware can be purchased in early American or colonial, traditional, and modern or _____ styles.

4. Common kinds of hinges include the butt, surface, cabinet, semiconcealed, pivot, piano, double-acting, _____, and dropleaf table hinges.

5. Common door catches include the friction, "snap grip," roller, magnetic, and _____.

6. Many kinds of lock sets and _____ are available to suit the style of every kind of door.

Checking Your Knowledge

1. Hardware should match the design of the furniture or home with which it is used. T or F

2. The correct hinge height for a 1 3/8-inch house door that is not over 32 inches wide is: (a) 1 1/2″, (b) 2 1/4″, (c) 3″, (d) 3 1/2″.

3. The height of a hinge includes the tips of the pins. T or F

4. The best hinge for an exterior door is a ball-bearing hinge. T or F

5. A hinge that is slightly offset at the barrel is called _____.

6. In good house construction there should be _____ (number) hinges on each door.

7. In most sections of the United States, the bottom hinge on a door should be the following distance from the bottom edge: (a) 6″, (b) 7″, (c) 10″, (d) 12″.

8. For the top hinge, in most states it must be _____ inches from the jamb rabbet to the top edge of the barrel.

9. The purpose of the third hinge on a door is to keep the door in alignment and to prevent warping. T or F

10. The easiest kind of hinge to install is: (a) butt, (b) surface, (c) concealed, (d) dropleaf table.

11. Another name for the concealed hinge is the _____ hinge.

12. For a screen that must fold in either direction, use a _____ butt hinge.

13. Instructions for installing lock sets are furnished by the manufacturer. T or F

    _____

14. A piano hinge is good for a door that must serve as a desk top. T or F

    _____

15. The correct kind of hinge to use on doors that are fitted to cabinets without frames is: (a) surface, (b) pivot, (c) semiconcealed, (d) piano.

    _____

16. A lip (reveal overlay casework) door should be hung with _____ hinges.

    _____

17. For a door that is 1 3/4 inches thick and over 48 inches wide, install three hinges that are _____ inches in height.

    _____

18. Check the spelling of the following words. If correct, place a "C" in the space. If incorrect, give the correct spelling.

    a. Pivot

    _____

    b. Swagged

    _____

    c. Hardware

    _____

    d. Semiconcaeled

    _____

Name_____

Score_____

Study Guide No. 48
CABINETMAKING

Reviewing the Main Ideas

1. The art of making furniture, store fixtures, built-ins, windows, doors, and specialized products such as musical instruments, toys, and kitchenware is called _____.

2. Cabinetmaking is done by cabinetmakers and mill workers in manufacturing plants and by _____ on the job.

3. The five basic construction methods in cabinetmaking include the skeleton or leg and rail, box, _____ _____, carcass, and frame with cover.

4. There are three categories of casework construction including exposed-face frame, flush overlay, and _____ overlay.

5. Two types of exposed-face frame construction are flush and _____.

6. The three basic methods of producing stock for large areas or surfaces are the glued-up stock; man-made wood materials such as plywood, particle board, or hardboard; and _____ or frame construction.

7. Some common types of doors are the flush door in an exposed-face frame, lipped door with an exposed-face frame, doors for _____ overlay design and reveal overlay design, drop door, and sliding door.

8. Common types of drawers include the _____ drawer, lipped drawer in an exposed-face frame, and drawer for flush overlay.

9. Common drawer guides include the lower corner guide and runner, the side guide and runner, the center guide and runner, and commercial metal guides. The best drawer guide to use is a _____ guide and runner.

10. Common details in furniture construction require fastening tops of tables and _____ and installing adjustable shelves and commercial legs.

11. Some of the steps in assembling _____ include assembling the parts and checking them, fastening the parts with glue and screws, clamping the parts, and checking the assembly.

12. Built-in cabinet work differs from furniture construction because it must be fitted to walls which are not usually _____ or square.

Checking Your Knowledge

1. Cabinetmaking is *not* done in one of the following places: (a) cabinet shops, (b) mill rooms, (c) door and window factories, (d) box factories.

2. Leg and rail or skeleton construction is *not* found in one of the following kinds of furniture: (a) chairs, (b) chests, (c) tables, (d) benches.

3. The mortise-and-tenon joint is the most common joint for leg and rail construction. T or F

_____

4. A box consists of four sides with the grain running in opposite directions. T or F

_____

5. A box turned on its side or end is _____ construction.

_____

6. The major difference between case and carcass construction is the amount of internal detail. T or F

_____

7. Stock for gluing up larger surfaces should not be more than _____ to _____ (inches) wide.

_____

_____

8. In arranging pieces for gluing up larger widths, you should *not:* (a) have the grain run in the same direction, (b) match the color and grain, (c) join the pieces with the rings on the end in the same direction, (d) saw off pieces that do not fit properly.

_____

9. A major difficulty in using plywood is the edge treatment. T or F

_____

10. Panel construction is *not* found in: (a) doors, (b) chairs, (c) desks, (d) case construction.

_____

11. The vertical pieces of a panel frame are called _____.

_____

12. The upper and lower horizontal pieces of a frame are called _____.

_____

13. A shorter vertical member dividing a panel is called a _____.

_____

14. Panel construction warps less than solid pieces. T or F

_____

15. One of the following is *not* a common method of leg-and-rail construction: (a) blind mortise-and-tenon, (b) dowel and corner block, (c) miter, (d) open mortise-and-tenon.

a

b

_____

16. In case work, all solid partitions or dividers should be dadoed into the other members. T or F

17. Identify these methods of covering the edges of plywood. Fig. 48-1:

c

a. _____

b. _____

c. _____

d. _____

e. _____

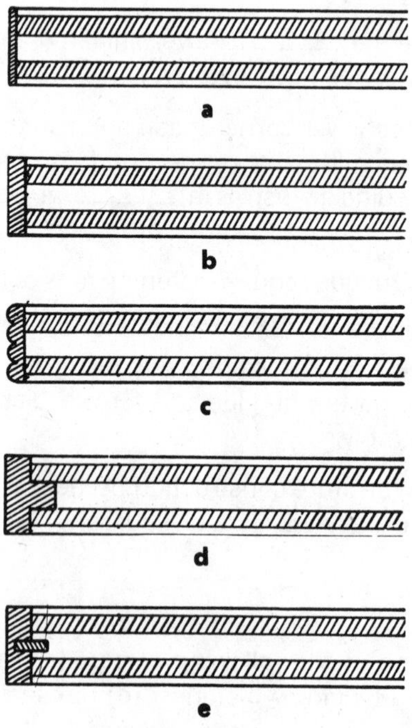

d

18. The length of dowels on a stile and rail door should be approximately the same as the _____ of the stiles.

19. The inside edge of stiles and rails that are shaped is called _____.

e

Fig. 48-1.

_____

20. A mullion is an intermediate rail. T or F

_____

21. One of the following is *not* a good joint to use in panel construction: (a) dowel, (b) open mortise-and-tenon, (c) butt, (d) stub mortise-and-tenon.

_____

22. Before installing a piece of plywood in a panel, be sure to _____ the edges.

_____

23. In installing a back on a unit that is to fit against the wall, the rabbet should be cut a depth of _____ to _____ (millimetres).

_____

_____

24. The corners of chairs and tables are often given extra strength by: (a) installing splines, (b) using screws, (c) installing corner blocks, (d) using special glue.

_____

25. In best furniture construction, dust panels are made with a thin plywood or hardboard center. T or F

_____

26. Small triangular pieces of wood that are glued and/or nailed in place at two adjoining members to give added strength are called _____ _____.

_____

27. For a flush door in an exposed-face frame, _____ hinges or surface hinges can be used.

_____

28. Butt hinges on a flush door in a frame make a fine appearance but require careful fitting. T or F

_____

29. A lipped door is very difficult to fit since it covers the frame of the door itself. T or F

_____

30. With a lipped door, _____ hinges are usually installed.

_____

31. When installing doors for flush overlay design, _____ hinges are often used.

_____

32. The most common hinge to use with a drop door is the _____ hinge.

_____

33. When space is limited or when regular doors take up too much room, _____ doors are best.

_____

34. For a 1' or 2' (305 to 610 mm) door, a _____ (inches) butt hinge would be satisfactory.

_____

35. One of the following is *not* a common joint used to join the back to the sides of drawers: (a) butt, (b) rabbet, (c) miter, (d) rabbet-and-dado.

_____

36. The best joint for fastening the front of a drawer to the sides is called a _____ joint.

_____

37. Name the parts of a drawer. Fig. 48-2:

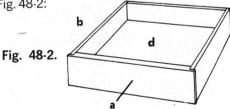

Fig. 48-2.

a. _____

b. _____

c. _____

d. _____

38. The entire drawer should be built of the same kind of wood. T or F _____

39. There should be _____ (inches) clearance for each side of the drawer. _____

40. The back of the drawer should be _____ (millimetres) narrower than the front. _____

41. The best material for drawer bottoms is _____ or plywood. _____

42. One of the following is *not* a common joint for joining the front to the sides of a drawer: (a) the drawer lock or corner joint, (b) the dovetail joint, (c) the finger joint, (d) the rabbet joint. _____

43. When the case or carcass is made without a frame, the best joint for the front of the drawer is the _____ _____ joint. _____

44. The best drawer guide is the center drawer guide and runner. T or F _____

45. Drawer guides and runners should be painted or finished. T or F _____

46. For heavy drawers, it is a good idea to install special metal guides. T or F _____

47. Identify these common methods of fastening tops to tables and cabinets. Fig. 48-3:

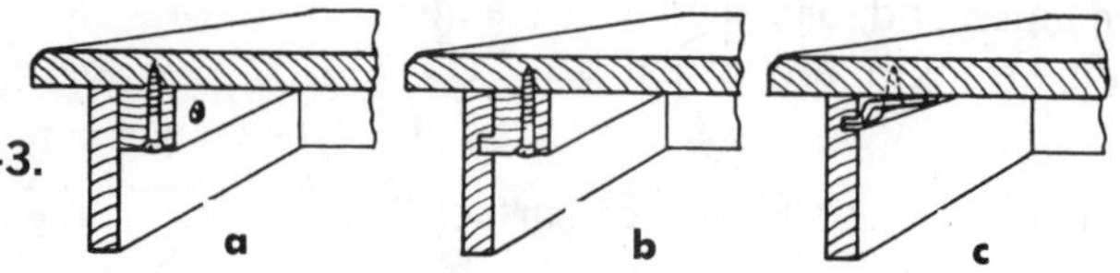

Fig. 48-3.

a. _____
b. _____
c. _____

48. Identify these common methods of installing adjustable shelves. Fig. 48-4:

Fig. 48-4.

a. _____
b. _____
c. _____
d. _____

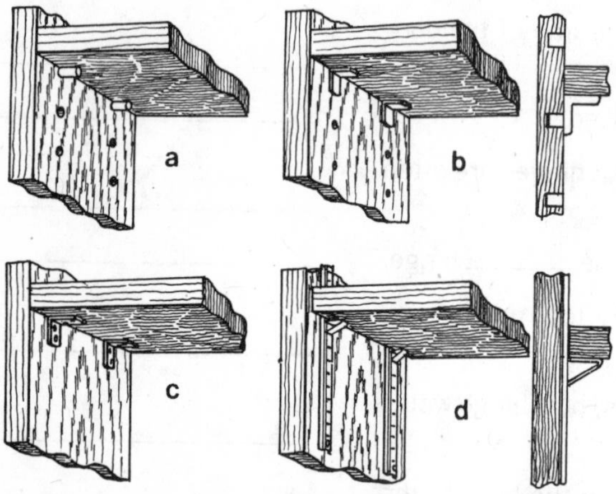

49. Another name for the dropleaf table joint is the _____ joint.

50. On the edge away from the hinge side there should be a slight _____ on the door.

51. In fitting a flush door, it is necessary to try the door in the opening several times. T or F

52. Fig. 48-5 shows a method of checking for _____.

Fig. 48-5.

_____

_____

_____

53. Fig. 48-6 shows a method of checking for _____.   _____

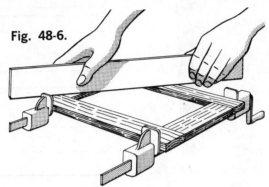

Fig. 48-6.

54. Identify the parts of a typical panel or frame. Fig. 48-7:

a. _____

b. _____

c. _____

d. _____

e. _____

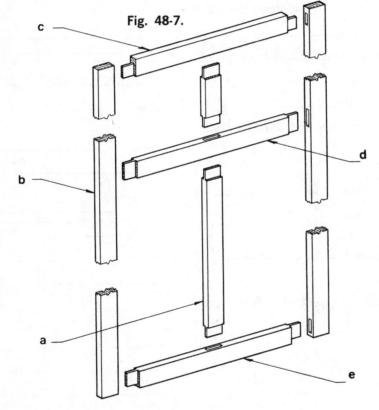

Fig. 48-7.

55. Name the standard stickings. Fig. 48-8:

a. _____

b. _____

c. _____

Fig. 48-8.

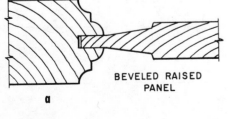

BEVELED RAISED PANEL

a

STRAIGHT PANEL

b

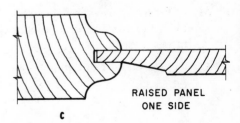

RAISED PANEL ONE SIDE

c

56. The joint shown in Fig. 48-9 is a _____ _____ joint.

57. In Fig. 48-58 in the text, the depth of the built-in is _____ inches.

58. In Fig. 48-58 in the text, the width of the center section is _____ inches.

59. In the second drawer unit shown in the text in Fig. 48-61, there are _____ (number) small drawers and _____ (number) large drawers.

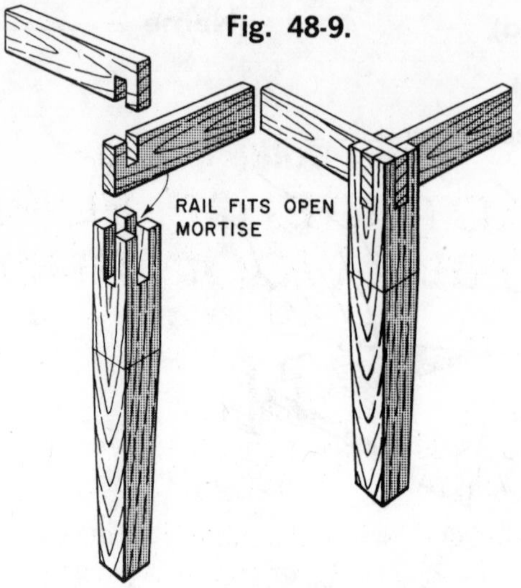

Fig. 48-9.

RAIL FITS OPEN MORTISE

60. Study Fig. 48-64a, b, c, d, and e in the text; then answer these questions:

    a. The kind of wood used for this built-in is _____.

    b. The thickness of the adjustable shelves is _____ inches.

    c. The metal screen used is made of _____.

    d. The exterior frame in section B-B is made of _____.

    e. The overall depth of the frame for the drawer unit shown in Section B-B is _____ feet and _____ inches.

    f. The total height of the stool shown in section C-C is _____ and _____ inches.

    g. The overall size of the top of the stool is _____ x _____.

61. Check the spelling of the following words. If correct, place a "C" in the space. If incorrect, give the correct spelling.

    a. Cabinetemaking

    b. Carcass

    c. Mulleon

    d. Haunched

172

Study Guide No. 49
MANUFACTURE OF FURNITURE AND OTHER WOOD PRODUCTS

Reviewing the Main Ideas

1. As a _____ material, wood is a natural product and, therefore, has many variable features such as grain pattern, density, and color.

   _____

2. Many specialized production _____ are used in the furniture industry. Among the more common ones are the double planer and surfacer, gang ripsaw, automatic lathe, shapers, and boring machines.

   _____

3. The first step in making furniture in a factory is _____, which includes making sketches, drawings, experimental models, and process route sheets.

   _____

4. Exact steps in producing furniture vary, but they commonly include conditioning the raw material, making lumber core plywood, cutting and machining, bending, laminating, fitting and _____, finishing, and upholstery.

   _____

5. The most common method of planning the laying out of furniture and cabinetwork is with the process _____ sheet, usually prepared in the factory's engineering department.

   _____

Checking Your Knowledge

1. The problems in furniture manufacturing are much the same as in the manufacture of metal products. T or F

   _____

2. The double planer and surfacer does the work of a jointer and a planer. T or F

   _____

3. A tenoner is made as either a single- or _____-end machine.

   _____

4. The tenoner's only use in furniture manufacture is to make the tenon for the mortise-and-tenon joint. T or F

   _____

5. A double-end cutoff saw is very similar to a double-end tenoner. T or F

   _____

6. An automatic lathe can be used to shape the irregular fronts of doors and other rectangular parts. T or F

   _____

7. A molding machine or sticker is very similar to a _____.

   _____

8. Boring machines are made either as vertical or horizontal. T or F

   _____

9. The first step in designing new furniture is to make sketches showing possible designs. T or F

   _____

10. The second step in designing furniture is to make an elevation or a front view drawing of each new piece. T or F

   _____

11. The scale used for elevation drawing is usually _____ inches equals one foot.

12. A sample of the new piece of furniture is built by skilled craftsmen in the sample or experimental room. T or F

13. A process route sheet is similar to a plan-of-procedure sheet. T or F

14. Lumber for furniture is purchased surfaced two sides. T or F

15. Lumber for furniture is kiln dried before it is used. T or F

16. Furniture factories keep raw lumber at a moisture content of from _____ to _____ percent before processing it.

17. Most furniture manufacturers make their own lumber core plywood. T or F

18. Solid stock is *not* used for structural parts in one of the following kinds of furniture: (a) legs, (b) rails, (c) table tops, (d) arms.

19. Pieces of furniture that must be carved, machined, and shaped are made of lumber core plywood. T or F

20. Mortise-and-tenon joints are more common than dowel joints in furniture production. T or F

21. Furniture factories have a special department for bending and laminating. T or F

22. Fitting and assembling furniture is done by the skilled hand woodworker. T or F

23. Unfinished pieces of furniture are called white wood. T or F

24. One of the following is *not* a material used for the lamp table, Fig. 49-38 in the text: (a) mahogany, (b) walnut, (c) gum, (d) oak.

25. The complete top of the lamp table measures 27″ x 20 1/2″ (686 x 521 mm). T or F

26. Item No. 9 of the lamp table is made of _____ wood.

27. The finished or net size of the drawer front of the lamp table is _____ inches in thickness, _____ inches in width, and _____ inches in length.

28. The total height of the lamp table is _____ (inches).

29. There is a separate route sheet for each major part that goes into a piece of furniture. T or F

30. In the average furniture factory, about _____ percent of all the lumber used ends up in the furniture.

31. The molding machine is sometimes called a: (a) shaper, (b) sticker, (c) jointer, (d) tenoner.

32. Identify some of the common kinds of cuts and joints that can be made on the double-end tenoner. Fig. 49-1:

a. _____

b. _____

c. _____

d. _____

e. _____

f. _____

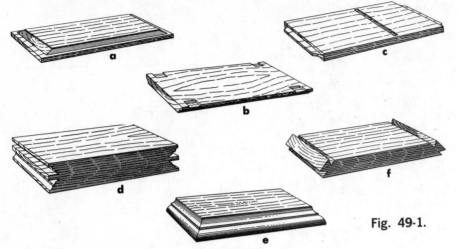

Fig. 49-1.

33. Check the spelling of the following words. If correct, place a "C" in the space. If incorrect, give the correct spelling.

a. Teniner

b. Stickar

c. Process

_____

_____

_____

Name_____

Score_____

Study Guide No. 50
PATTERNMAKING

Reviewing the Main Ideas

1. Patternmaking is the art of building a wood form or _____ that is used in the foundry.

2. The most common method of making _____ is called green-sand molding.

3. Some of the common terms you must be acquainted with include mold, simple pattern, _____ pattern, dowel, shrinkage, draft, and fillet.

4. The best woods for patterns are white pine, mahogany and _____.

5. A simple pattern is a _____-piece pattern.

6. Most pattern drawing should be dimensioned in _____ since this work is part of the metal and plastics industries.

7. A core box is needed when a casting must be made that has an opening in it. The _____ is formed in the core box.

8. Patterns that are mounted on a plate are called a match _____.

Checking Your Knowledge

1. The two parts of a flask are the _____ and the _____.

2. When molten metal cools, it: (a) expands, (b) shrinks, (c) cracks, (d) softens.

3. All patterns for foundry are made of wood. T or F

4. One of the following is not a common wood used for patterns: (a) pine, (b) oak, (c) mahogany, (d) cherry.

5. Taper on a pattern that allows it to be pulled out of the sand easily is called: (a) fillet, (b) draft, (c) drag, (d) shrink.

6. A pattern made of two or more parts that can come apart is called a _____ pattern.

7. A pattern is placed on a board with the tapered side up. T or F

8. The shrink rule used for aluminum should be _____ inch per foot longer than a standard foot.

9. Fillets are not made of one of the following materials: (a) wax, (b) wood, (c) glass, (d) leather.

10. The pattern is placed on the _____ board as a first step in ramming a mold.

Woodworking for Industry Student Guide
John L. Feirer—Copyright © 1979

11. Molten metal is poured into the hole formed by the _____ pin.

12. A riser pin should be tapered. T or F

13. A piece of material used to round off the inside sharp corners of a pattern is called a _____.

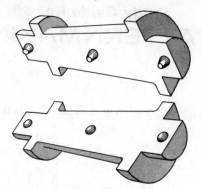
Fig. 50-1.

14. A piece of hardened sand that is inserted in a mold to shape an interior opening is called a: (a) cope, (b) core, (c) fillet, (d) dowel.

15. Dowel pins used on a split pattern should be: (a) 1 1/2 x diameter, (b) 2 x diameter, (c) 3 x diameter, (d) 4 x diameter.

16. The pattern shown in Fig. 50-1 is called a _____ pattern.

17. A simple way to find the amount of metal needed for a solid pattern is to weigh the pattern and then multiply that weight by the factor given in Fig. 50-2.

    a. If the pattern is made of pine and weighs 12 ounces, give the weight of the brass casting in pounds.

    b. Tell the cost of the casting if brass for castings costs 67¢ a pound.

FACTORS

Pattern Material	Casting Materials					
	C. S.	C. I.	Brass	Copper	Zinc	Alum.
Pine	17.0	16.0	19.0	19.6	15.0	5.70
Mahogany	13.0	12.0	14.0	14.7	11.5	4.50
Cherry	11.5	10.5	12.5	13.0	10.0	3.80

Fig. 50-2.

18. The pattern for the small anvil (Fig. 50-3), was made of mahogany and weighs 2 ounces. Tell how much the aluminum would cost for 60. The price of aluminum is 50¢ a pound.

Fig. 50-3.

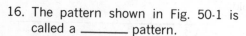
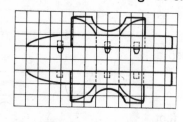

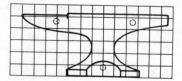

19. An aluminum casting weighs 2.85 pounds. Give the weight of the pine pattern for this part.

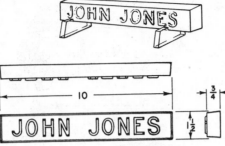

_____

20. Fifty students wish to make their own pattern for the nameplate (Fig. 50-4). Give the number of board feet of pine the group will need. (Use actual sizes and add 20 percent for cutting.)

Fig. 50-4.

_____

21. Write the words that these phrases describe:

    a. The upper section of a flask.

    _____

    b. Slight taper given to a pattern so it can be drawn from the sand.

    _____

    c. A metal or wood frame with an open top and bottom in which the mold is formed.

    _____

22. When a core is made from sand and a binder and then hardened, it is called a _____ core.

    _____

23. The pattern color for machined surfaces is _____.

    _____

24. The finish allowance for gray cast iron is _____ (millimetres).

    _____

25. A shrink rule for gray cast iron has an allowance of _____ (inches) per foot.

    _____

26. In the new code, the pattern color for core prints is _____.

    _____

27. Identify these items used in foundry. Fig. 50-5:

    a. _____

    b. _____

    c. _____

    d. _____

    e. _____

    f. _____

    g. _____

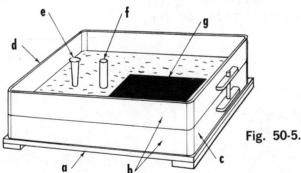

Fig. 50-5.

28. Patterns of a circular shape are built of rows of wood pieces called _____.

    _____

29. The best boards for circular patterns are plain-sawed. T or F

    _____

30. Check the spelling of the following words. If correct, place a "C" in the space. If incorrect, give the correct spelling.

    a. Drafte

    b. Drag

    c. Flasck

    d. Cope

    e. Moldeing

_____

_____

_____

_____

_____

Name_____

Score_____

Study Guide No. 51
BOATBUILDING

Reviewing the Main Ideas

1. In boatbuilding most of the layout cutting, and fitting is done on _____ surfaces.

2. Some of the common terms used in boatbuilding include batten, chine, mold, stringers, bow, _____, transom, keel, planking, and decking.

3. In boat drawing there are three main views of the _____, namely, the profile view or side elevation, the plan view, and the body plan.

4. In boatbuilding, solid lumber of mahogany, oak, and spruce, and marine plywood and _____ plywood are commonly used.

5. The steps in building a boat depend on the size and construction. For the dinghy in the text, steps are layout, _____, install side and bottom planks, finish detail, and apply a finish.

Checking Your Knowledge

1. The following number of people actively enjoy boating and other water activities: (a) less than 5 million, (b) 10 million, (c) 15 million, (d) more than 30 million.

2. All items needed to build a boat can be purchased in kit form. T or F

3. The following is an order for mahogany plywood for building a boat: 2 pieces, 3/8″, 5-ply, 24″ x 72″, veneer-core, African mahogany, good one side, Type 1 glue @ $1.35 per square foot.

   a. The width of the plywood in feet is _____.

   b. The thickness of the plywood is _____ inch.

   c. The plywood is made of _____ pieces of veneer.

   d. The total number of square feet is _____.

   e. The total cost is _____.

4. The standard panel size for plywood is _____ (millimetres) x _____ (millimetres).

5. Only exterior grades of plywood should be used in boatbuilding. T or F

6. If steel screws were used to assemble a boat for saltwater use, the screws would _____.

7. Fittings made of one of the following materials *cannot* be used in salt water: (a) brass, (b) bronze, (c) galvanized steel, (d) Monel Metal®.

8. Match the descriptions at the left to the boatbuilding terms at the right:

   a. the shape or frame around which the boat is built
   b. back crosspiece of boat
   c. the part farthest forward
   d. piece where sides and bottom join
   e. the main piece that extends the length of the bottom
   f. the outer shell
   g. a strip of wood used to cover cracks

   1. planking
   2. keel
   3. bow
   4. mold
   5. batten
   6. chine
   7. transom

   a. _____
   b. _____
   c. _____
   d. _____
   e. _____
   f. _____
   g. _____

9. Answer these questions about the 7' 9" pram dinghy shown and described on text pages 653–661.

   a. The chines should be made of _____.

   b. The correct wood for the keel is _____.

   c. The overall height of the mold for Station 2 is _____ inches.

   d. The overall width of the mold for Station 1 is _____ inches.

   e. The boat has _____ seats.

   _____
   _____
   _____
   _____
   _____

10. Give the numbers of screws, by sizes, needed for the pram dinghy.

    a. No. 6—5/8" F. H.

    b. No. 8—3/4" F. H.

    c. No. 8—1" F. H.

    d. No. 10—1 1/4" F. H.

    e. No. 12—1 1/2" F. H.

    _____
    _____
    _____
    _____
    _____

11. Tell how many square feet of 1/4-inch plywood are needed for planking for the pram dinghy.

12. If mahogany costs $1.50 per board foot, figure the keel cost for the pram dinghy.

    _____

    _____

13. Name the items described below:

    a. A shape or form around which the boat is built.

    b. The main wood piece that extends the entire length of the bottom of the boat.

    c. The back crosspiece of a boat.

    _____

    _____

    _____

14. Check the spelling of the following words. If correct, place a "C" in the space. If incorrect, give the correct spelling.

    a. Planking

    b. Batton

    c. Corrosion

    d. Marene

    _____

    _____

    _____

    _____

Study Guide No. 52
BUILDING A HOUSE

Reviewing the Main Ideas

1. Steps in building a house are as follows: stake out the site, excavate the cellar, erect the framing, complete the exterior, install utilities, and complete the _____.

2. A builder must be sure the lot is wide and _____ enough for the house.

3. Homes are sometimes built without basements; instead they are built on _____ slabs.

4. Windows are installed in _____ openings.

Checking Your Knowledge

1. One of the following is *not* an important step in getting ready to build: (a) evaluating the lot, (b) choosing the house plan, (c) staking out the house, (d) securing the financing.

2. The architect's fee for a home usually ranges from _____ to _____ percent of the total building cost.

3. The cost of a lot should not exceed _____ to _____ percent of the total building budget.

4. You should obtain one bid from a building contractor when preparing to build a house. T or F

5. One of the following is *not* a common method of providing a foundation for a home: (a) cement slab, (b) partial basement, (c) full basement, (d) galvanized steel slab.

6. The basement of a home is usually dug by hand. T or F

7. Footings should be from _____ to _____ inches wider than the walls.

8. Footings should rest on fill dirt. T or F

9. Foundations often are either of poured concrete or cement block. T or F

10. The outside of a cement-block foundation wall should be treated to make it waterproof. T or F

11. Another name for a girder is a _____.

12. If boards are used for the subfloor, they should be nailed in line with the floor joists. T or F

13. Members of several different trades often work on a house at the same time. T or F

14. Windows should be given a coat of paint before they are installed in the openings. T or F

15. The metal put across the tops of windows for preventing leaks is called _____.

16. When gypsum board or panel is used for the interior of the home, it is called _____ construction.

17. When rock lath and plaster are used, it is called _____ construction.

18. A house should cost no more than _____ to _____ times the owner's annual income.

19. The basement ceiling height of the home should be no less than _____.

20. Chimneys should extend at least _____ feet above the roof peak.

21. The attached garage should have a _____-resistant wall and ceiling.

22. The worker shown in the text in Fig. 52-11 is the _____.

23. Answer these questions concerning Fig. 52-2 in the text.

   a. The overall size of this house is _____ x _____.

   b. The windows used in the bedrooms of this house are of the _____ type.

   c. The living room measures _____ x _____.

   d. There are _____ (number) bedrooms in this house.

   e. The width of the storage area just off the hall is _____.

   f. There are _____ (number) convenience outlets in the larger bedroom.

   g. The size of the front door is _____ x _____.

24. Study the floor plan in the text in Fig. 52-3 and answer these questions:

   a. There are _____ (number) bedrooms in this home.

   b. The size of the living room is _____ x _____.

25. Check the spelling of the following words. If correct, place a "C" in the space. If incorrect, give the correct spelling.

   a. Excavating

   b. Utilaties

   c. Horizontal

184

Name_____

Score_____

Study Guide No. 53
CARPENTRY TOOLS, MATERIALS, AND METHODS

Reviewing the Main Ideas

1. Homes of wood-frame construction include those that are enclosed with wood _____, wood shingles, brick veneer, and stucco.

2. The three major kinds of wood-frame construction used today are platform frame, _____ frame, and plank-and-beam.

3. Carpenters today must know how to use all types of hand _____ and power equipment.

4. Finish (select) grades are used for _____ and exterior trim.

5. Each trade association modifies the American Lumber Standards for its own _____ rules.

6. The quality of a house depends to a large degree on how well the parts are _____ together.

7. It is important to protect lumber and other materials from the _____ when they are on the building site.

Checking Your Knowledge

1. Of every 10 homes built in the United States, _____ (number) are of wood-frame construction.

2. A house covered with brick veneer or stucco is a wood-frame house. T or F

3. One of the following is *not* a common kind of wood-frame construction: (a) platform frame construction, (b) balloon frame construction, (c) eastern frame construction, (d) plank-and-beam construction.

4. The construction method most commonly found in one-story homes is platform construction. T or F

5. In plank-and-beam construction, the ceiling height is measured to the upper side of the plank. T or F

6. The carpenter's two most common measuring and testing tools are the _____ _____ and _____.

7. In using a carpenter's level, the term "level" is to horizontal as _____ is to vertical.

8. Lumber for house construction is ordered by the "_____" sizes.

9. A 20d nail is _____ inches long.

10. There are about _____ (number) 9d nails in a pound.

11. It takes about _____ pound of nails to case a window.

12. Identify the three methods of nailing. Fig. 53-1:

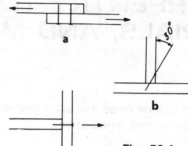

a. _____

b. _____

c. _____

13. The kind of frame construction most commonly used in pre-fabrication is _____ _____ construction.

14. The nailing schedule for attaching a rafter to a plate calls for _____ (number) nails of _____ size.

Fig. 53-1.

15. Identify these parts of a platform frame construction house. Fig. 53-2:

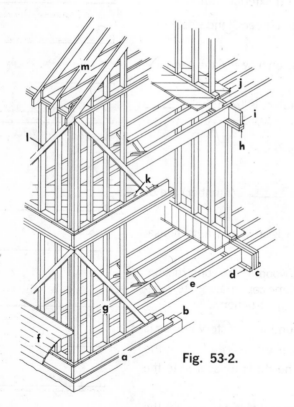

Fig. 53-2.

a. _____

b. _____

c. _____

d. _____

e. _____

f. _____

g. _____

h. _____

i. _____

j. _____

k. _____

l. _____

m. _____

16. The nailing schedule to end-nail top plates to studs calls for the use of two nails of _____ size.

17. Approximately _____ (number) of 4d nails make up a pound.

18. A 12d nail is shorter than a 10d nail. T or F

19. In making built-up girders and beams of wood, use _____ (size) nails that are nailed at 32 inches on center.

20. The two parts of a carpenter's square are the _____ and the _____ .   _____

                                                                                                                                                      _____

21. The table on a square that gives the number of board feet in different sizes of boards is called the _____ board measure table.   _____

22. Name the parts of a house constructed by the plank-and-beam method. Fig. 53-3:

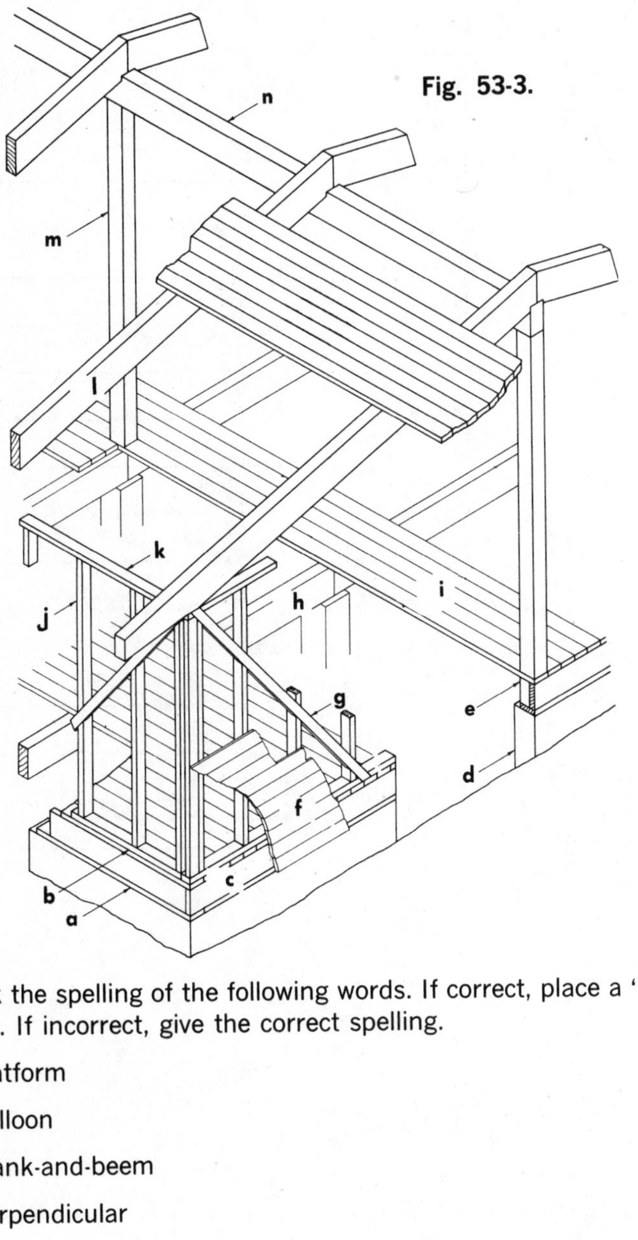

a. _____

b. _____

c. _____

Fig. 53-3.

d. _____

e. _____

f. _____

g. _____

h. _____

i. _____

j. _____

k. _____

l. _____

m. _____

n. _____

23. Check the spelling of the following words. If correct, place a "C" in the space. If incorrect, give the correct spelling.

a. Platform

_____

b. Balloon

_____

c. Plank-and-beem

_____

d. Perpendicular

_____

Study Guide No. 54
FLOOR AND WALL FRAMING

Reviewing the Main Ideas

1. The mason is responsible for putting in the footings and the basement wall, but a _____ should know how it is done.

2. The exact location of a house is determined by local _____.

3. Excavation of the basement area may be done with a _____ loader, power shovel, or similar equipment.

4. In building basement walls, the _____ act as the base of the foundation.

5. Poured concrete walls can be damp-proofed with one coating of cold or hot tar or _____.

6. Basement walls are made of either 8″ or 12″ concrete blocks or of solid (poured) _____.

7. The kind of floor framing in a home depends on whether it is _____ frame or balloon frame construction.

8. The most important parts of floor _____ include the posts, girders, sill plate, joists, headers, trimmers, bridgings, and subflooring.

9. The framing of the _____ wall consists of a sole or soleplate, studs, headers, top plates, and firestops.

10. There are three common methods of assembling studs at the _____ corner: three studs and space blocks, three studs and shim, or three studs.

11. The two common ways of assembling studs where partitions meet the _____ wall are using two studs spaced close together or using a nailing strip.

12. Framing around the _____ requires special care because of the danger of fire.

13. The exterior walls of the house are covered with _____.

14. The common types of materials used for wall sheathing are boards, plywood, structural insulating board, and _____ sheathing.

15. There are two common types of _____ framing: bearing and non-bearing.

16. A building system that uses less materials and cost less to construct is the _____ 24 framing system.

Checking Your Knowledge

1. The footings for a home should extend below the frost line. T or F

2. The size of footings depends on local soil conditions and building _____.

3. Concrete blocks commonly used for basement walls measure _____ or _____'' x _____'' x _____''.

4. When a series of building materials is installed with one layer over another, such as shingles, siding, or cement blocks, the layers are often called _____.

5. In laying a concrete-block basement wall, the _____ block should be laid first.

6. Anchor bolts should be placed _____ to _____ feet apart.

7. A wood or metal member used in the basement to support a girder is called a _____.

8. When beams are made of wood, they should be nailed together with two rows of _____d nails.

9. No wood post should be used that is smaller than 6'' x 6'' in size. T or F

10. In floor framing, the lowest member of the frame structure, the one that rests on the foundation, is called a sill or _____ _____.

11. There are two types of wood-sill construction used over foundation walls. T or F

12. In house construction, the sills are laid directly on the _____.

13. The parallel beams which support floor and ceiling loads are called _____.

14. One of the following is *not* a common size for floor joists: (a) 2'' x 6'', (b) 2'' x 10'', (c) 2'' x 12'', (d) 2'' x 16''.

15. Joists are usually placed _____ inches on center.

16. A beam placed at right angles to a joist is called a _____.

17. One of the following is *not* a common type of bridging: (a) diagonal wood bridging, (b) solid bridging, (c) plastic bridging, (d) metal bridging.

18. Bridging helps stiffen the floor and distribute the load evenly on a joist. T or F

19. If plywood is used for subflooring, it should be _____ inch thick.

20. Subflooring boards that are laid at right angles to the joist are the best base for installing the floor. T or F

21. Boards used for subflooring should be no wider than _____ inches.

22. Identify the common parts of this exterior wall. Fig. 54-1:

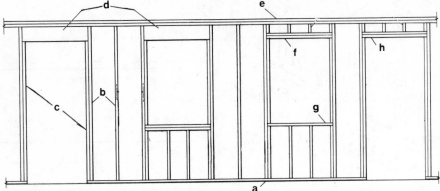

Fig. 54-1.

a. _____

b. _____

c. _____

d. _____

e. _____

f. _____

g. _____

h. _____

23. A slender wood member placed in a vertical position as a supporting part of a wall or partition is called a _____.

24. Another name for a header is a _____.

25. Bridging is *not* usually made from short pieces of material of the following size: (a) 1″ x 3″, (b) 1″ x 4″, (c) 2″ x 4″, (d) 2″ x 2″.

26. The lower end of bridging is not nailed until the _____ has been installed.

27. The ends of diagonal bridging are cut at an _____.

28. When framing a window, if the span does not exceed three feet, _____ _____ can be used to fasten the ends of headers to the studs.

29. The most common method of assembling a wall section is to do it in a _____ position on the subfloor.

30. Floor joists should be spaced 10″ apart. T or F

31. The sole or soleplate is a piece of lumber that usually measures _____″ x _____″.

32. A single top plate is used in most home construction. T or F

33. In one-story buildings, sills and plates serve as fire blocking. T or F

34. The two common ways of laying boards for subflooring are _____ and at right angles to the joists.

35. Standard spacing for stud walls is 16″ or 24″ on center. T or F

_____

_____

_____

_____

_____

_____

_____

_____

_____

_____

_____

36. Identify the three kinds of outside corners. Fig. 54-2:

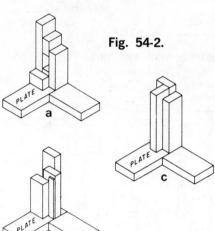
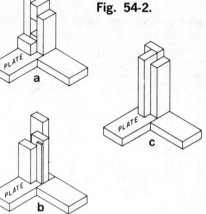
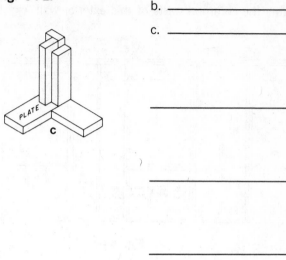

Fig. 54-2.

a. _____

b. _____

c. _____

37. Bearing partitions must be made of 2 x 4s set with the wide dimension perpendicular to the partition. T or F

_____

38. Studs in bearing partitions that support floors should be placed _____ inches on center.

39. Studs for the bearing partition that supports ceiling and roof should be placed _____ inches on center.

_____

40. Non-bearing partitions can be made of studs that measure 2″ x 3″. T or F

_____

41. Identify the parts of the first-floor framing in a platform-frame construction. Fig. 54-3:

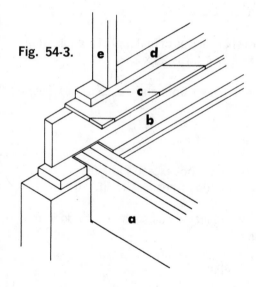

Fig. 54-3.

a. _____

b. _____

c. _____

d. _____

e. _____

42. Identify the two methods of assembling studs where partitions meet exterior walls, as shown in text Fig. 54-37.

a. _____

b. _____

43. Sills should be well anchored to the _____ with bolts.

_____

44. The bolts should be spaced _____ to _____ feet apart.

_____

45. Girders used in a home are made of _____ or _____.

_____

46. Girders that are glued together are called _____ members.

_____

47. Both ends of the bridging should be nailed before the subfloor is installed. T or F

_____

48. Trenches for footings should always go below: (a) the dew line, (b) the frost line, (c) the gravel line, (d) the bottom line.   _____

49. A piece of metal between the top of the footing and the sill plate is called a _____ shield.   _____

50. Short crosspieces of wood between the floor joists that strengthen the total floor are called: (a) supports, (b) firestops, (c) bridging, (d) boosters.   _____

51. The width of the footing in text Fig. 54-3a is: (a) 8″, (b) 9″, (c) 12″, (d) 15″.   _____

52. Holes must be drilled in the sill plate for the _____ to go through.   _____

53. In most areas it is necessary to add a piece of nonferrous metal between the top of the foundation and the sill plate to protect the wood from: (a) frost, (b) flies, (c) termites, (d) bees.   _____

54. Floor joists are usually placed 16 inches on center. T or F   _____

55. Plywood can be used for subflooring. T or F   _____

56. A piece that is installed at the top of a window opening is called a _____.   _____

57. Subflooring is laid directly over _____.   _____

58. The thickness of boards used for subflooring should not be less than _____ inch.   _____

59. The purpose of a subfloor is to provide a base for a _____ floor.   _____

60. Subflooring may be laid in two ways: (a) parallel or diagonal to the joist, (b) at right angles or diagonal to the joist, (c) parallel or at right angles to the joist, (d) none of these.   _____

61. The most common practice is to nail the wall parts together while they are flat on the subfloor and then raise the unit. T or F   _____

62. Top plates are nailed directly to the studs. T or F   _____

63. Studs are added to a wall after the wall has been put up. T or F   _____

64. The plate should be nailed to the studs with two _____d nails.   _____

65. Studs are usually placed _____ or _____ inches on center.   _____

66. A beam placed over a window opening is called a _____.   _____

67. One of the following is *not* a common material used as sheathing for exterior walls: (a) plywood, (b) wood sheathing, (c) structural insulating board, (d) plastic laminates.   _____

68. Greater stability can be given to the walls of a house when using boards for sheathing by installing them _____ to the framing.   _____

69. All wood materials must be at least _____ inches away from the outside face of chimney and fireplace masonry.   _____

70. A wood mantel must be at least _____ inches away from the fireplace opening.

_____

71. Check the spelling of the following words. If correct, place a "C" in the space. If incorrect, give the correct spelling.

   a. Joice

   _____

   b. Girder

   _____

   c. Bridgeing

   _____

   d. Trimmers

   _____

   e. Header

   _____

Name_____

Score_____

Study Guide No. 55
BUILDING THE ROOF

Reviewing the Main Ideas

1. The process of building the roof is called roof _____.

2. The traditional method of roof framing is to install a ridge board and _____. The newer method uses trussed rafters.

3. The framing members which support the finished ceiling are called ceiling _____.

4. The seven most popular roofs for homes and small buildings are flat, shed, gable, hip, gable with dormer, gable and valley, and _____ and valley roof.

5. Another name for a _____ roof is a lean-to roof.

6. The framing of a gable roof consists of a ridge board and _____ rafters.

7. The distance from one side of the building to the other is called the _____.

8. In a regular gable roof, the amount equal to half the span is called the _____.

9. The vertical distance from the top of the plate to the upper end of the measuring line is called the _____.

10. An imaginary line running lengthwise along the middle of the rafter is called the _____ line.

11. The ratio of the rise of the rafter to the span or width of the building is called the _____.

12. A horizontal piece that connects the upper ends of the rafters is called a _____.

13. The overhanging part of a rafter is called a _____.

14. The skeleton of the roof is formed by the rafters. A right triangle is formed by the _____, the run, and the rafter.

15. The table on one side of the carpenter's square for figuring rafters is called the _____ table.

16. Other names for the top cut of a common rafter are the _____ cut and the ridge cut.

17. Other names for the bottom cut are the plate cut, the _____ cut, and the bird's-mouth cut.

18. The length of the rafter as shown on the rafter table must be reduced by half the thickness of the _____ board. (See text, Fig. 55-13.)

19. Boards of 1″ x 6″ size installed in the upper third of the attic space to every third pair of rafters are called _____ beams.

20. A second method of laying out a common rafter is to make a _____ pattern of it on the subfloor of the house.

21. A third method involves _____ _____ the length of a common rafter with the square. (See text, Fig. 55-19.)

22. The fourth method of finding the length of common rafters is to multiply the _____ of the building by a certain decimal.

23. A rafter that extends from the corner of the building diagonally to the ridge is called a _____ rafter.

24. A rafter that forms a depression in the roof is called a _____ rafter.

25. The length of hip and valley rafters can be found on the rafter table of the _____ square.

26. The discontinued rafter is a _____ rafter.

27. A rafter consisting of an assembly of members forming a rigid framework of triangular shapes is called a _____ rafter.

28. The material that covers a roof directly over the rafters is called _____.

29. A projection of the roof at the eaves that forms a connection between the roof and side walls is called a _____.

30. The trim along the gable end of a house is called the _____ section.

31. Thin metal sheets placed around chimneys, roof valleys, and over windows and doors are called _____.

32. Common materials used for _____ roofs are wood, asphalt, or asbestos shingles.

33. Unless the eave projection is 24″ or greater, there is need for _____ and downspouts.

34. The low-pitched gable roof usually has built-up roofing with a topping of gravel, crushed _____, or marble chips.

35. It is often necessary to ventilate attic space with _____.

Checking Your Knowledge

1. The part of the roof that extends from the plate to the ridge board is called a _____.

2. Rafters are usually spaced _____ or _____ inches on center.

3. Ceiling joists are used as a tie between exterior walls and interior partitions. T or F

4. The vertical distance from the top of the plate to the upper end of the measuring line is called the _____.

5. The distance between one side of the building and the other is called the _____.

6. Identify these common kinds of roofs. Fig. 55-1:

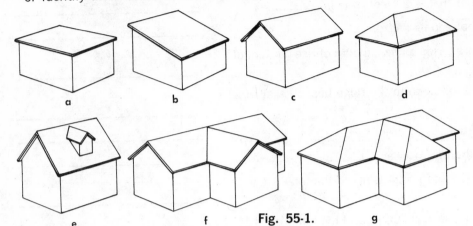

Fig. 55-1.

a. _____
b. _____
c. _____
d. _____
e. _____
f. _____
g. _____

7. Name the roof framing terms shown in Fig. 55-2:

Fig. 55-2.

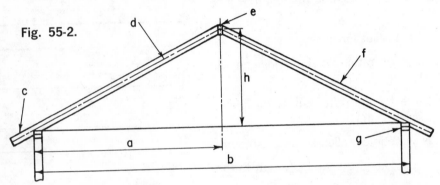

a. _____
b. _____
c. _____
d. _____
e. _____
f. _____
g. _____
h. _____

8. The rise of a roof with a span of 20 feet and one-fourth pitch is _____ feet.

9. The rise of a roof with a span of 24 feet and one-fourth pitch is _____ feet.

10. The pitch of a roof with a 20-foot span and 10-foot rise is _____.

11. The three most common roof pitches are:

　　a. _____ pitch, or _____ inches to a foot.

　　b. _____ pitch, or _____ inches to a foot.

　　c. _____ pitch, or _____ inches to a foot.

12. The rise of a roof with a 24-foot span and one-third pitch is _____ feet.

13. The rise of a roof with a 26-foot span and one-half pitch is _____ feet.

_____

_____

_____

_____

_____

_____

_____

_____

14. The ratio of the rise of the rafter to the span or width of the building is called the _____.

15. The pitch of a roof with a 30-foot span and a 15-foot rise is _____.

16. The rise of a one-half-pitch roof that is 24 feet wide is _____.

17. The rise of a one-half-pitch roof equals half the _____.

18. The rafter tables on a square are based on the amount of rise per foot of _____.

19. A rafter that extends from the top plate to the ridge board is called a _____ rafter.

20. Rafters are the _____ of a roof.

21. A right triangle is formed by the run, rise, and _____.

22. Find the rise per foot of run if the span is 24 feet and the total rise is 8 feet.

23. Find the rise per foot of run if the span is 20 feet and the total rise is 10 feet.

24. Find the rise per foot of run if the span is 20 feet and the total rise is 5 feet.

25. Find the length of the common rafter in feet for question No. 24.

26. One of the following is *not* the name for the rafter cut at the ridge board: (a) top, (b) plumb, (c) ridge, (d) bird's-mouth.

27. One of the following is *not* the name for the rafter cut at the plate: (a) bottom, (b) heel, (c) plumb, (d) plate.

28. The notch formed by the heel cut is sometimes called a _____ mouth.

29. Boards measuring 1″ x 6″ that are used to give added strength to the rafters are called _____ _____.

30. Rafters that extend diagonally from the plate to the ridge at a point where two roof sections intersect are called _____ rafters.

31. Give the names of the parts shown in this hip roof. Fig. 55-3:

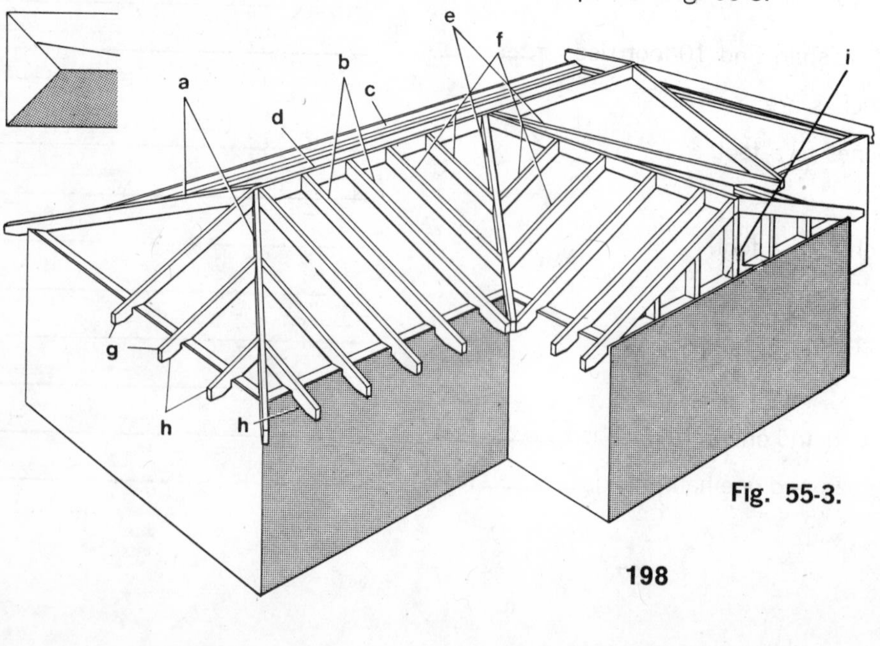

Fig. 55-3.

a. _____
b. _____
c. _____
d. _____
e. _____
f. _____
g. _____
h. _____
i. _____

32. Jack rafters lie in the same plane with common rafters. T or F

    _____

33. Jack rafters are usually spaced 18″ apart. T or F

    _____

34. Rafters that do not extend from the plate to the ridge are called _____ rafters.

    _____

35. The rafter tables on a square are used to find: (a) ridge line, (b) measuring lines, (c) length per foot of run, (d) length per foot of span.

    _____

36. The length of common rafter per foot of run for one-fourth pitch is: (a) 13.42″, (b) 19.00″, (c) 17.82″, (d) 25.34″.

    _____

37. The top cut and the heel cut are always at _____ angles to each other.

38. Side cuts for jack rafters are found on the fifth line of the rafter table on the steel square. T or F

    _____

39. The piece of wood added to every third rafter to increase strength is called: (a) rafter beam, (b) collar beam, (c) ridge beam, (d) joist beam.

    _____

40. Plywood used for roof sheathing should be _____ inch thick.

41. The four types of cornices are:

    a. _____

    b. _____

    c. _____

    d. _____

42. The flat board with molding located at the outer face of the cornice is called a _____.

    _____

43. One of the following is *not* a common material used for flashings: (a) galvanized iron, (b) manganese, (c) copper, (d) aluminum.

    _____

44. Flashing should be installed directly over a window. T or F

    _____

45. Many kinds of materials are used for roof coverings. T or F

    _____

46. Collar beams are installed only in the upper sixth of attic space. T or F

    _____

47. Hand-cut wood shingles are called _____.

    _____

48. Most wood shingles are made of _____ _____ (type) wood.

    _____

49. Chimneys and dormers always need flashing. T or F

    _____

50. The high side of a chimney should have a metal covered saddle. T or F

    _____

51. Find the length of the common rafters in the following problems. *Do not* adjust for the thickness of the ridge boards.

    a. Rise 6 feet and run 12 feet.

    _____

    b. Rise 6 feet and span 12 feet.

    _____

    c. Pitch one-third and rise 6 feet.

    _____

    d. Rise 8 feet and run 8 feet.

    _____

    e. Pitch one-fourth and span 20 feet.

    _____

52. Find the length of hip rafter on a hip roof if the building is 20 feet wide and 30 feet long and the roof has one-fourth pitch.

53. Check the spelling of the following words. If correct, place a "C" in the space. If incorrect, give the correct spelling.

a. Measureing line

b. Pitch

c. Discontinued

d. Soffite

e. Fassia

f. Friege

g. Ventilation

Name_____

Score_____

Study Guide No. 56
COMPLETING
THE EXTERIOR AND INTERIOR

Reviewing the Main Ideas

1. Much of the _____ of a house depends on the kinds and styles of materials used to complete the exterior and interior.

2. The normal _____ of interior doors is 1 3/8 inches. A normal thickness for an exterior door is 1 3/4 inches.

3. A doorjamb consists of two side jambs and a _____ jamb.

4. The material around a door is called _____ or trim.

5. Door hinges should be about 10 to 11 inches from the bottom and 5 to 7 inches from the _____, with a center hinge between them.

6. A window in which two sash slide up and down in grooves in the frame is called a _____ window.

7. The rough or _____ opening for a window is shown on the house plans or is included in instructions given by the manufacturer.

8. The trim around the inside of a window is called the _____.

9. The horizontal piece that laps the sill of the window is called the _____.

10. The trim just below the window stool is called the _____.

11. The pieces that hold the window sash in place are called _____.

12. Siding is a covering commonly used on the _____ of a house. Common siding materials include wood shingles, plywood, and hardboard.

13. The most common styles of siding are _____, drop, board-and-batten, and tongue-and-groove.

14. Nails to install siding should be made of galvanized steel or _____.

15. The common corner treatment for siding includes _____ boards, mitered corners, metal corners, or alternately lapped corners.

16. Moisture vapor that travels through the wall of the house can cause such painting problems as blistering, peeling, and staining on the _____ wall.

17. Common types of insulation include _____, batt, fill, reflective, and rigid.

18. The two common kinds of stairways are straight, continuous run and stairway with a _____ platform.

19. The stringer provides support for the _____.

20. In designing a stairway, the total distance from one floor to the next is called the _____ _____.

21. The total horizontal length of the stairs is called the _____ _____.

22. The vertical face of a step is the riser; the horizontal face is the _____.

23. The interior walls and ceilings are either _____ or dry-wall construction.

24. The most common materials used for _____ construction are gypsum board, plywood, fiberboard, hardboard, and paneling.

25. Ceiling tile is often used as an _____ material.

26. Common materials used for _____ of homes are hardwood, tile, and plywood.

27. Interior trim is installed around doors, windows, and as a _____ molding at the floor and wall intersections.

28. Kitchen cabinets and built-ins are really a form of _____.

Checking Your Knowledge

1. Identify these common door styles. Fig. 56-1:

Fig. 56-1.

a. _____

b. _____

c. _____

d. _____

a

b

(Fig 56-1 continued on page 203)

Fig. 56-1.

c

d

2. Where a ventilated area is necessary, a _____ door is installed.

_____

3. The major difference between interior and exterior doors is in the _____.

_____

4. The most common thickness for interior doors is _____ inches.

_____

5. The main entrance door should be _____ feet wide.

_____

6. The main entrance door should be _____ feet _____ inches high.

_____

_____

7. Other exterior doors may be _____ inches wide.

_____

8. Doorjambs for standard plaster walls should be _____ inches wide.

_____

9. The rough opening for doorjambs should be _____ inches wider and _____ inches higher than the size of the door.

_____

_____

10. Doorjambs should be nailed to the studs with _____d finishing nails.

_____

11. Casing around doors is sometimes called _____.

_____

12. The joint at the upper corners in installing the casing around a door is called a: (a) butt, (b) miter, (c) dovetail, (d) rabbet.

_____

13. The stop on the hinge side of the door should have about _____ inch clearance to keep the door from scraping on the stop.

14. Identify these common kinds of windows. Fig. 56-2:

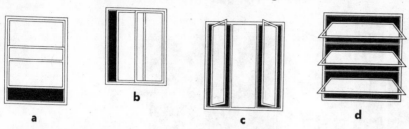

Fig. 56-2.

a. _____
b. _____
c. _____
d. _____
e. _____
f. _____

15. The most common type of window is the _____ window.

16. Name the parts of the window trim. Fig. 56-3:

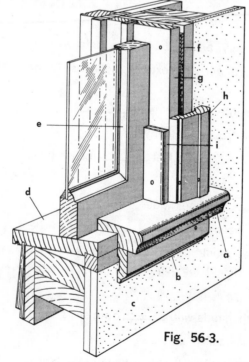

Fig. 56-3.

a. _____
b. _____
c. _____
d. _____
e. _____
f. _____
g. _____
h. _____
i. _____

17. A wood window should be primed after it has been installed. T or F

18. The horizontal piece that laps the sill of the window and projects beyond the casing is called the _____.

19. The trim piece just under the window stool, which is nailed to the stool, is called the _____.

204

20. The rough opening for a double-hung window should be 10 inches larger in each direction than the glass size. T or F

21. Casing or trim and door stops are nailed to the _____.

22. Material used for doorjambs is usually of _____ inch nominal thickness.

23. A door 2′ 6″ x 6′ 8″ would require a rough opening of _____ inches in width and _____ feet _____ inches in height.

24. Identify these common kinds of siding. Fig. 56-4:

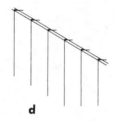

a

b

c

d

Fig. 56-4.

a. _____

b. _____

c. _____

d. _____

25. Exterior woodwork should be at least _____ inches above the ground.

26. The nails used for exterior woodwork should be either galvanized steel or _____.

27. The ends of siding should be given a heavy coat of _____ _____.

28. Identify these common corner treatments. Fig. 56-5:

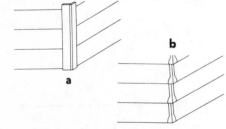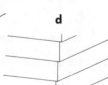

a

b

Fig. 56-5.

c

d

a. _____

b. _____

c. _____

d. _____

29. The bottom of siding should be even with the top trim over door and window openings. T or F

30. When tongue-and-groove siding is used, it should be blind nailed to the wood sheathing at _____-inch intervals.

31. When applying shingles in a single course, the nails should be driven in about _____ (inches) above the butt line of the following course.

32. It is important to have a vapor barrier on the warm side of walls. T or F

33. Appliances that add a great deal of moisture to the air of a house are the dishwasher and _____.

34. One of the following is *not* a common type of insulation: (a) batt, (b) reflective, (c) blanket, (d) powder.

35. The total distance from one floor to the next is called the _____ _____.

36. The total horizontal length of stairs is called the _____.

37. The vertical face of one step is called the _____.

38. The total of one riser and one tread should be not much less than _____ inches and not more than _____ inches.

39. If the riser is 8 inches, the maximum length of tread should be _____ inches.

40. Identify these parts of a stairway. Fig. 56-6:

Fig. 56-6.

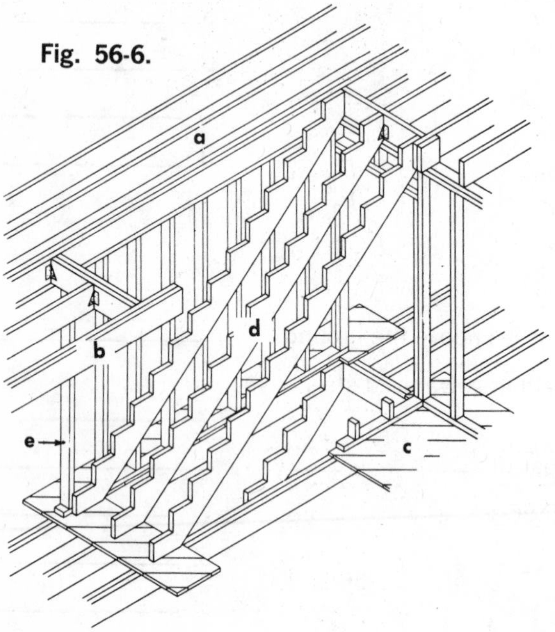

41. In dry-wall construction, the walls do not need to be plastered. T or F

42. Plastered walls usually are given two coats of plaster, a _____ coat and a _____ coat.

43. Sheet material composed of gypsum filled with paper is called _____ _____.

44. It is necessary to tape and seal the joints in dry-wall construction. T or F

45. If wall-to-wall carpet is to be used, the finished floor may be a good grade of _____.

46. Before installing a hardwood floor, cover the _____ with building paper.

47. The first course of a hardwood floor should be laid about _____ inch from the side wall.

48. Hardwood flooring should be nailed every _____ to _____ inches.

_____

_____

_____

_____

_____

a. _____

b. _____

c. _____

d. _____

e. _____

_____

_____

_____

_____

_____

_____

_____

_____

49. The correct size nail for 25/32-inch flooring is a _____d or _____d nail.

_____

_____

50. The joints in hardwood flooring should line up. T or F

_____

51. The angle for toenailing flooring should be about _____ degrees.

_____

52. Base molding of a house consists of two parts, the _____, or baseboard, and the base shoe (shoe mold).

_____

53. When installing a tile floor, border tile should be not less than _____ a tile in width.

_____

54. A fitted joint used at the corner of a base is called: (a) mitered joint, (b) coped joint, (c) trimmed joint, (d) corner joint.

_____

55. The standard height for a sink-base cabinet is _____ inches.

56. The vertical distance between a sink cabinet and a wall cabinet should be _____ inches.

_____

57. If there are 32 square feet of rock lath to a bundle, give the number of bundles needed for a new room that measures 12' x 16' with an 8-foot ceiling. Count walls and ceiling.

_____

58. Tell the number of pieces of 9'' x 9'' tile that would be needed for the floor of a room that measures 10' x 12'.

_____

59. Figure how many pieces of 4' x 8' sheet rock would be needed to cover the walls and ceiling of an 8-foot high room that measures 14' x 16'.

_____

60. Check the spelling of the following words. If correct, place a "C" in the space. If incorrect, give the correct spelling.

    a. Luover

_____

    b. Jalouise

_____

    c. Reflective

_____

    d. Stringer

_____

    e. Casemunt

_____

Name_____

Score_____

Study Guide No. 57
BUILDING A GARAGE

Reviewing the Main Ideas

1. The house design should largely determine the _____ of the garage. _____

2. The location of the garage can be determined by making measurements from the house itself or from the _____ line. _____

3. Consult a lumber dealer when working out your plans and _____ lists for a garage. _____

4. The cement for the footings of a garage should be poured directly into the _____ in the earth. _____

5. The foundation for the garage should be about three _____ high. _____

6. A slab of poured concrete should be used for the garage _____. _____

7. The garage wall consists of a soleplate, studs, and _____ plates. _____

8. After they are assembled and nailed together on the ground, the _____ may be raised into position. _____

9. The exterior wall should be covered with _____ of fiberboard or plywood. _____

10. The skeleton of the garage roof consists of rafters and a _____ board. _____

11. The frame for the door is called a _____. _____

12. Windows for a garage should match or basically blend with those in the _____. _____

13. If boards are to be used for roof sheathing, they should be 1″ x 6″. To complete the roof, apply a layer of 15-pound felt and then asphalt _____. _____

14. Complete the exterior of the garage by adding the _____ and metal corner caps. Also add trim around windows and doors. _____

Checking Your Knowledge

1. A complete packaged garage is available from many lumber yards. T or F _____

2. A packaged garage consists of lumber cut to size, doors, _____ hardware, and all the other materials needed. _____

3. The design of the garage should be influenced by the design of the house. T or F _____

4. The footing for a garage should be about 2 to 3 inches in depth. T or F _____

5. Crushed stone or gravel should cover the earth to a depth of _____ to _____ inches before adding the concrete. _____

6. The cement floor should be made with ready-mix concrete and poured to a depth of _____ inches.

7. The cement floor should be reinforced with No. _____ wire mesh.

8. There are two methods of assembling the walls. T or F

9. Fiberboard is another name for insulation board. T or F

10. Ceiling joists for the garage should be of _____ x _____ material.

11. For applying the shingles, use a _____-inch galvanized roofing nail.

12. The trim boards to cover under the rafters and box in the eaves should be _____ x _____ material.

13. The plywood or fiberboard used to sheath the exterior walls should be large boards. T or F

14. Doorjambs must be level and _____ before nailing.

15. Roofing boards must be cut to exact length before they are nailed in place. T or F

16. In installing an overhead garage door, always follow the _____ instructions.

17. If the garage is 20 feet wide, the roof is 1/2 pitch and the ridge board is 3/4 inch, give the exact length of the rafters (without allowing for the tail).

18. Check the spelling of the following words. If correct, place a "C" in the space. If incorrect, give the correct spelling.

    a. Raffter

    b. Plum cut

    c. Ridge board

Study Guide No. 58
MANUFACTURED HOUSING

Reviewing the Main Ideas

1. A slow and expensive way to build a home by the traditional method is to use _____ pieces of lumber and other building materials.

2. A large, essential part of a house such as a wall section or roof trusses is called a _____.

3. The standard size of big sheet material, such as plywood, insulation board, and gypsum wallboard is _____ x _____. Sheets this size are meant for use on 16-inch or 24-inch stud spacing.

4. A uniform unit of measurement, such as 4 inches or 4 feet, used in building a house is called the _____ or standard dimension.

5. The construction of the skeleton of the roof with the roof _____ is an important part of a production-line house.

6. Beams made of lumber and plywood that are hollow in the center are called _____ beams.

7. Component units made up to 2 x 4s, fir plywood sheets, and insulation, all nailed and glued together, are called _____ skin panels.

8. Only a small portion of a componentized house is mass produced. The shell of the house will be about _____ to _____ percent of the total cost.

9. There is variation from community to community in the building standards or _____. In many communities the building standards are out of date.

10. Lumber mills will precut standard-_____ lumber for studs, headers, and other framing parts.

11. In manufacturing components for a home, the house sections are assembled on standard _____.

12. In assembling, framing, and attaching exterior and interior surfaces, power-operated _____ and stapling equipment is used.

13. The component parts that are being manufactured are being carried along by a _____ system.

14. A factory-assembled, nonpermanent structure usually 8 to 14 feet wide is a _____ home.

Checking Your Knowledge

1. Four-by-eight-foot sheets are made to use on _____-inch or _____-inch stud spacing.

2. One of the following is *not* listed as an advantage of using roof trusses instead of joists in rafters: (a) they are cheaper, (b) they close in a house more rapidly, (c) the house can be finished as one large area, (d) partitions do not have to be load-bearing.

3. A house in which a roof truss system is used instead of joists in rafters gives a great deal more flexibility in interior layouts. T or F

4. Box beams are high in strength and stability and relatively low in weight and cost. T or F

5. A stressed-skin panel consists of:

   a. A top skin of _____-inch plywood.

   b. Eight-foot stringers of _____ x _____-inch material, set 16 inches on center.

   c. Insulation that is _____ inches thick.

   d. A bottom skin of _____-inch plywood.

6. Sectional (modular) housing refers to units fabricated in _____ sections.

7. A factory-assembled, three-dimensional section of a building to be shipped to a site is called a _____.

8. In building an average three-bedroom home, approximately _____ percent of the expense is for plumbing, including the kitchen and bath.

9. A mobile home is a structure that is at least _____ feet long.

10. Building codes are standard from community to community in the United States. T or F

11. In manufacturing the components of a house, parts are held together during assembly by the use of _____.

12. In manufacturing homes in a factory, a _____ system is used to carry the parts along.

13. Mobile homes are built on a heavy wheeled _____ which can be moved.

14. Trailers, campers, and motorized homes are designed for highway use. T or F

15. The heating, air conditioning, and wiring in an average-size home costs approximately the following percent of the total cost: (a) 5 percent, (b) 10 percent, (c) 20 percent, (d) 40 percent.

16. The most common shape of sectional (modular) housing is a rectangular unit with 3-to-1 or _____ proportions.

212

17. Check the spelling of the following words. If correct, place a "C" in the
space. If incorrect, give the correct spelling.

    a. Stressed skin   _____

    b. Moduler   _____

    c. Factory   _____

Name_____

Score_____

Study Guide No. 59
BUILDING A MODEL HOUSE

Reviewing the Main Ideas

1. A great deal about building construction can be learned by building a miniature or _____ house. A standard set of house plans should be followed.

   _____

2. The best scale for building a miniature or model house is one that is 1 1/2″ = 1′, or _____ full size.

   _____

3. For fastening joists, headers, and other large members, use 5/8- or 3/4-inch _____.

   _____

4. The lumber used for a miniature house can be cut from poplar, pine, redwood, or other _____ species.

   _____

5. A good base for a miniature house is 3/4-inch plywood or _____ board.

   _____

6. A 2 x 4 for a miniature house should measure _____ x _____, which is actually a little larger than scale.

   _____

   _____

7. The rafters should be nailed to one of the top plates so that the entire _____ can be removed.

   _____

8. Good material for making shingles is _____.

   _____

9. Sheathing for the house can be made from thin _____.

   _____

Checking Your Knowledge

1. A good scale for building a miniature house is _____ inches equals one foot.

   _____

2. The nails that are best for nailing joists, headers, and other large members of a miniature house are _____-inch or _____-inch long.

   _____

3. One of the following is not a common material used for building a miniature house: (a) poplar, (b) pine, (c) oak, (d) redwood.

   _____

4. A good foundation for a miniature home is _____-inch plywood or a particle board sheet.

   _____

5. The experience of cutting, fitting, and nailing is the same in building a real house as in building a miniature house. T or F

   _____

6. For attaching shingles to a miniature house, use staples or _____-inch nails.

   _____

7. In building a miniature house, it is a good idea to nail the two top plates together so that the entire roof can be removed. T or F

   _____

8. Check the spelling of the following words. If correct, place a "C" in the space. If incorrect, give the correct spelling.

a. Architeceral

b. Skale

c. Fondation

_____

_____

_____

Name _____

Score _____

Study Guide No. 60
FINISHING TOOLS AND METHODS

Reviewing the Main Ideas

1. The woodworking occupations do not include those of _____ and finishing wood products.

2. A painter must know how to prepare the surface and apply paint and also be able to select and _____ paints and match colors.

3. A furniture finisher must be able to do all of the steps required to apply a _____ to a good piece of furniture.

4. In furniture factories, finishing is broken down into a series of _____ that require less skilled labor than is required of a finisher.

5. A person who removes and camouflages all types of defects is called a finish _____.

6. Some of the materials used for filling nail holes, cracks, and defects include _____ wood, stick shellac, wood dough, sawdust and glue, and patching plaster.

7. Common brushes used to apply paints and finishes include the varnish and enamel brush, wall brush, utility brush, and _____ brush.

8. There are two types of roller _____, one that is dipped in the paint and the other self-feeding.

9. Industrial finishes applied with a _____ gun amount to about 85 or 95 percent of all commercial finishing.

10. When the air and fluid are mixed outside the gun, it is called an _____-mix gun.

11. If all spraying is done in a spray booth that is properly ventilated, there is no need for a _____.

12. The spray gun has two adjustments, one for regulating the fluid flow and the other for changing the _____ pattern.

13. When using a spray gun, hold it 6 to 8 inches from the surface. Keep the gun at _____ degrees to the surface being sprayed.

14. Banding is a process of spraying vertical or horizontal sections with a slight overlapping of each _____.

15. When spraying corners, aim the gun directly at the edge so that _____ of the spray goes on either side.

16. After each spraying, the gun should be cleaned thoroughly using a _____.

Checking Your Knowledge

1. Painting and finishing, strictly speaking, are two woodworking occupations. T or F

2. A skilled worker who repairs and camouflages defects is called a furniture finisher. T or F

3. One of the following is *not* a material that can be used to fill holes and cracks in wood surfaces: (a) paste, (b) stick shellac, (c) wood dough, (d) plastic wood.

4. Plastic wood closely resembles unfinished wood. T or F

5. When making a crack or hole filler with sawdust and powder glue, mix the material with water. T or F

6. Identify these common paint brushes. Fig. 60-1:

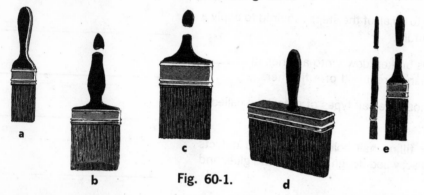

Fig. 60-1.

a. _____
b. _____
c. _____
d. _____
e. _____

7. Stick shellac is applied with: (a) the fingers, (b) a warmed putty knife, (c) a dry roller coater, (d) a flatting brush.

8. The correct solvent for a varnish brush is a solution of _____ turpentine and _____ varnish.

9. Industrial finishes are usually applied with a spray gun. T or F

10. The device that controls air pressure and removes dirt from a spray gun is called a transformer. T or F

11. Hoses sometimes connect the spray gun with the paint (or _____) container.

12. When spraying in a spray booth, it is always necessary to wear a respirator. T or F

13. When spraying, the gun should be kept at a distance of _____ to _____ inches from the surface.

14. When holding a spray gun, tip it at a slight angle to the surface. T or F

15. Each stroke of the spray gun should overlap the last by about _____ percent.

16. When spraying corners, direct the gun so that about 70 percent goes to one side and 30 percent to the other. T or F

17. The holes in the spray gun cap should be cleaned out with a sharp wire. T or F

18. Furniture factories have one person to do all of the work in finishing a piece of furniture. T or F

19. A varnish or enamel brush is usually about _____ to _____ inches wide.

20. The correct solvent for shellac is

_____.

21. Lacquer finishes are used on approximately _____ percent of all furniture items.

22. A device that delivers air at high pressure to operate a spray gun is called a

_____.

Fig. 60-2.

23. Identify these two types of gun tips. Fig. 60-2:

a. _____

b. _____

24. Check the spelling of the following words. If correct, place a "C" in the space. If incorrect, give the correct spelling.

a. Finishing

b. Finish patsher

c. Compresor

d. Transformer

e. Suction

Name _____

Score _____

Study Guide No. 61
HOME FINISHES

Reviewing the Main Ideas

1. The material that cements wood cells together is called _____.

2. Most wood finishes help prevent _____.

3. A highly recommended finish for hardwood floors is _____ varnish.

4. A type of finish that can be applied successfully to wood with a moisture content of up to 15 percent is _____ finish.

5. A commercial wood filler is often used on hardwoods to fill the _____.

6. If softwoods show a marked contrast between springwood and summerwood, the first step is to apply a _____.

7. A stain that tends to raise the grain is _____ stain.

8. A stain that dries more slowly than spirit stains is _____ stain.

9. A clear finish which is a natural resin dissolved in alcohol is _____.

10. Paints are composed of two basic materials, the pigment and the _____.

11. A paint that contains binders that are either soluble in or dispersed in water is _____ paint.

12. An easy way to stain plywood is to apply one coat of a combination of wax and _____.

13. The most commonly used hardwood for residential flooring is _____.

14. Floor sealers can be applied by brush or as a _____.

15. Exterior finishes can be classified either as penetrating or _____.

16. A special mixture of a modified, semitransparent oil-based stain for western red cedar can be made by the _____ formula.

17. Painting should be done in dry weather when the temperature is above 7 degrees _____.

18. The deterioration of oil-based paints generally follows _____ (number of) stages.

19. The moisture content of a wood door should be stabilized at or near room _____.

20. Wood windows, sash, and frames can be obtained factory-treated with water-repellent _____.

21. Basement walls consisting of a concrete slab placed on the ground should have a _____ barrier under the slab.

22. A common paint problem caused by excessive moisture in the walls is blistering and _____.

23. Good-quality paints wear away normally in a period of four to _____ years.

24. When paint is applied too thick over too much oil, it may cause _____.

25. Finish coats usually cover from 500 to 600 square feet per _____.

26. Paint the side of a house _____ the sun has passed over it.

27. Masonry cracks should be filled with a _____ mixture.

Checking Your Knowledge

1. Unfinished wood weathers about the following amount per century: (a) 1/8″, (b) 1/4″, (c) 3/8″, (d) 1/2″.

2. An extremely high moisture content in wood due to long periods of dampness may cause decay. T or F

3. Latex enamels are not washable. T or F

4. One of the following is *not* a problem caused by resins and oils in green lumber: (a) blistering, (b) cracking, (c) dislodging the finish, (d) changing the overall color of the finish.

5. Latex finish can be used successfully on woods with moisture content up to: (a) 20 percent, (b) 15 percent, (c) 25 percent, (d) 30 percent.

6. Two materials that can be used to cover knots and pitch streaks are knot sealer or _____.

7. The physical structure of hardwoods is less complex than that of softwoods. T or F

8. One of the following hardwoods is *not* open-grained: (a) oak, (b) birch, (c) ash, (d) chestnut.

9. Color in woods such as cedar, redwood, walnut, and mahogany is due to the presence of: (a) moisture, (b) pores, (c) lignin, (d) tannin.

10. Softwoods require the use of a filler before finishing. T or F

11. One of the following is *not* a common solvent for stains: (a) water, (b) spirits, (c) gasoline, (d) oil.

12. Waxed surfaces can be repaired by spot cleaning with mineral spirits. T or F

13. Another common name for polyurethane varnishes is _____ varnishes.

14. Shellac is a natural resin dissolved in: (a) water, (b) oil, (c) alcohol, (d) gasoline.

15. Pigments are very thin liquids that provide color and hide the underlying surface. T or F

16. The word "volatile" means that the fluid evaporates slowly. T or F

17. Latex paint can be thinned with water. T or F

18. One of the following is *not* an advantage of water-based paint: (a) no solvent vapor, (b) slow-drying, (c) easy clean up, (d) spot touch-up.   _____

19. A simple method of staining plywood is to apply one coat of combined wax and stain. T or F   _____

20. Particle board has knots and a grain. T or F   _____

21. Factory-primed hardboard is available for purchase. T or F   _____

22. One of the following is *not* a common hardwood used for residential flooring: (a) oak, (b) pine, (c) birch, (d) maple.   _____

23. Before staining, oak floors should be filled to make sure the surface is completely smooth. T or F   _____

24. Floor sealers are inexpensive and provide protection from water damage and warping. T or F   _____

25. Exterior finishes such as paints and varnishes are considered to be the penetrating type. T or F   _____

26. Pigments in water-repellent preservative finishes help protect the wood surface from destruction by ultraviolet light. T or F   _____

27. Stains are a surface finish. T or F   _____

28. A formula that can be mixed to use as a finish on red cedar is called: (a) USDA, (b) Madison, (c) Forest Products Laboratory, (d) Agriculture Department.   _____

29. One of the following is *not* usually a cause of paint failures: (a) improper selection of paint, (b) poor construction, (c) using a bristle brush, (d) poor paint application.   _____

30. Painting should *not* be done in dry weather when the temperature is about: (a) 45 °F, (b) 7 °C, (c) 50 °F, (d) 0 °C.   _____

31. The third stage of the deterioration of oilbased paint is the _____ stage.   _____

32. Chalking types of paint are good to use in bright colors. T or F   _____

33. Clear exterior finishes prevent the penetration of ultraviolet light. T or F   _____

34. The most commonly used wood for shingles and shakes is ponderosa pine. T or F   _____

35. The best method of staining shakes or shingles is to immerse them in stain before installation. T or F   _____

36. Doors should be sanded before applying finish but not between the various coats of finish. T or F   _____

37. The top and bottom edges of a door should not be finished. T or F   _____

38. A wood commonly used for exterior doors is: (a) walnut, (b) mahogany, (c) oak, (d) cherry.   _____

39. When applying window finishes, cover the weatherstripping with a finish. T or F   _____

40. The finish should overlap the window pane about 1/8 inch to seal the glazing joint. T or F

41. The maximum of moisture content that wood should contain before finishing is: (a) 15 to 16 percent, (b) 18 to 20 percent, (c) 20 to 24 percent, (d) 12 to 24 percent.

42. Masonry basement walls should have mortar and asphalt coating on the outside. T or F

43. Exterior moisture damage can be reduced by using corrosion-resistant nails. T or F

44. Gutters and downspouts should be used on roofs that have eave projections of 23 inches or less. T or F

45. The most common cause of poor performance of exterior house paint can be traced to water in back of the paint film. T or F

46. Good-quality paints wear away normally in a period of four to _____ years.

47. Application of paint with too much oil can cause wrinkling. T or F

48. The number of square feet to be covered by painting is obtained by multiplying the average height of the house times the _____ of the house.

49. The average undercoat or primer will cover about _____ square feet.

50. Check the spelling of the following words. If correct, place a ''C'' in the space. If incorrect, give the correct spelling.

   a. Deterroration

   b. Varneshes

   c. Solvints

   d. Linseed

   e. Vehical

   f. Pigment

   g. Penetreting

   h. Cauking

Study Guide No. 62
FURNITURE FINISHING

Reviewing the Main Ideas

1. After a product is assembled, the surface must be prepared for _____. _____

2. Common materials used to fill dents and irregularities include _____ shellac, plastic wood, wood dough, and wood-sanding dust mixed with powdered glue. _____

3. A pure distillation of petroleum is called _____ _____. _____

4. The material derived from coal tar is called _____. _____

5. A colorless liquid made from petroleum is called _____. _____

6. The colorless liquid used as a solvent for shellac is _____. _____

7. Material made from the resin of pine trees is called _____. _____

8. The finishing material made from flaxseed is called _____ _____. _____

9. The process of removing color from wood in order to obtain a full-blond effect is called _____. _____

10. When no spraying equipment is available or when dust is a problem, it is good to apply a _____ finish. _____

11. Two common types of staining materials are _____ colors, or dyes, and insoluble pigment colors. _____

12. Water stains are made from _____. _____

13. A stain made by mixing dyes in the solvent of _____ and alcohol is called non-grain-raising stain. _____

14. Stains made by mixing dyes in alcohol are called _____ stains. _____

15. The most common type of oil stain used in school shops is _____ oil stain. _____

16. Finishing materials made from dyes and lacquers that can give a combined staining and sealing effect are called transparent lacquer _____. _____

17. The common washcoat for stains used in school shops is made of alcohol and _____. _____

18. In furniture manufacturing, when lacquer is used for a final finish, lacquer _____ are applied. _____

19. To fill the pores of open-grained wood, use a paste _____. _____

20. The process of adding a highlighted, shaded, or antiqued effect is called _____. _____

21. The most common finish used by furniture manufacturers is the _____ finish. _____

22. The final steps in applying a good finish are rubbing, polishing, and
_____.

_____

Checking Your Knowledge

1. A good finish will cover up mistakes in cabinetmaking. T or F

_____

2. Wet-dry abrasive paper used for wood finishing should be grades No.
_____ and _____.

_____

_____

3. Bleaching is a process for coloring wood. T or F

_____

4. One of the following reasons does _not_ explain why a water stain is good:
(a) it does not raise the grain, (b) it is relatively inexpensive, (c) it
penetrates the wood very well, (d) it accentuates the wood texture.

_____

5. Match the finishing supplies at the left to the descriptions at the right:

a. mineral spirits	1. resin from pine trees
b. benzene	2. made from flaxseed
c. benzine	3. powder from lava
d. alcohol	4. limestone
e. turpentine	5. paraffin oil
f. linseed oil	6. solvent for shellac
g. pumice	7. made from coal tar
h. rottenstone	8. colorless liquid from petroleum
i. rubbing oil	9. pure distillation of petroleum

a. _____

b. _____

c. _____

d. _____

e. _____

f. _____

g. _____

h. _____

i. _____

6. Before using pigment oil stain on end grain, apply some linseed oil.
T or F

_____

7. Before applying water stain, raise the grain of wood by sponging with
water. T or F

8. A good oil finish can be made from a mixture of two-thirds linseed oil and
one-third hot turpentine. T or F

_____

9. Stains are made from two kinds of coloring material, namely, soluble
colors, or _____, and _____ pigment colors.

_____

10. A stain made from dyes mixed in a solvent of glycol and alcohol is called a
_____.

_____

11. A transparent lacquer toner will both seal and stain the wood. T or F

_____

12. A good washcoat for most stains is a mixture of seven parts alcohol to one
part shellac, using a four-pound-cut shellac. T or F

13. Paste filler is _not_ needed on one of the following woods: (a) oak, (b) pine,
(c) walnut, (d) mahogany.

_____

14. When applying paste filler, brush with the grain, not across it. T or F

_____

15. Paste filler should be mixed to a consistency of _____.

_____

16. A highlighted, shaded, or antiqued effect is given to the surface of wood by _____.

17. Enough stain should be mixed at one time for the entire project. T or F

18. Clear brushing lacquer can be used on a piece of furniture. T or F

19. To obtain a satin finish on a surface, rub with _____ grade wet-or-dry abrasive paper.

20. Common materials used to fill small cracks and dents do *not* include: (a) stick shellac, (b) plastic wood, (c) varnish, (d) wood dough.

21. Excess glue should be sanded off before applying a finish. T or F

22. For simple bleaching operations _____ crystals can be dissolved in hot water.

23. A common material used for oil finishing includes a mixture of one-third _____ varnish, one-third boiled _____ oil, and one-third gum _____.

24. To get a walnut-colored oil for finishing, use one-half _____ brown and one-half _____ umber.

25. In furniture production in which lacquer is used as a final finish, a lacquer stain should be used for washcoating. T or F

26. A filler is needed for the following wood: (a) poplar, (b) fir, (c) ash, (d) pine.

27. Paste fillers are made from ground _____, linseed oil, turpentine, _____, and colors.

28. The best material for removing filler is either a coarse cloth or _____.

29. As a final protection for fine furniture, apply liquid wax. T or F

30. A natural maple finish requires no stain. T or F

31. Check the spelling of the following words. If correct, place a "C" in the space. If incorrect, give the correct spelling.

    a. Bleaching

    b. Turepentine

    c. Rottenstone

    d. Seeling

    e. Glazing